Walk
YOUR WAY
Calm

**A Guided Journal for Uncluttering
Your Mind with Every Step**

© 2021 by Hearst Magazines, Inc.

Illustrations by Malte Müller

Book design by Izzy Lamb

Library of Congress Cataloging-in-Publication Data is on file with the publisher.

ISBN 978-1-950099-99-3

Printed in China

2 4 6 8 10 9 7 5 3 1 paperback

HEARST

Walk
YOUR WAY
Calm

**A Guided Journal for Uncluttering
Your Mind with Every Step**

Jennifer Walsh
and the Editors of

Prevention

Contents

Part Three: Walking Wellness Tracker 236

THE
Path TO
Calm

have always looked at walking—and the ability to move my legs in any way—as a gift. My twin sister is disabled and in a wheelchair. She has never been able to walk. So, the simple act of moving my body forward, one foot in front of the other, has always provided me with a deep sense of gratitude, and throughout my life I have tried to make the most of every step.

I've spent much of my life as a marathon runner and triathlete. In my 30s and through half of my 40s, I had a dog, and she was my walking companion for 15 years. When we walked together, I always thought of it as something I needed to do for her, not me. But then a funny thing happened: After she passed away, I found myself walking even more than I did when she was alive. I kept going to the park, often twice a day, for long walks in all kinds of weather, from sunshine to rain to snow. I realized that all of this time the walks weren't just for her, but also for me. It was a profound realization.

On my walks, I began noticing the plants and flowers around me like I hadn't before. I would continuously photograph the changing landscape (it didn't hurt that my local park is one of the most recognizable in the world, Central Park in New York City). My walks made me feel calm, and I just enjoyed them for myself. It wasn't until 2016, when I was filming my interview series, *Walk with Walsh*, that I realized something else. Each person I interviewed would say how great the walk felt and how nice it was to be outside during the workday. They would inevitably mention how they never got outside. It shocked me, and I wondered: If people knew that going for a walk outside felt good, why were they not doing it more often?

This inspired my research and work in bridging brain health and the power of walking in nature. The more science and data I uncovered, the more I wanted to share with others the impact I was discovering. I began leading what I call "Wellness Walks" all over the country and around the world, from Italy to Spain, for individuals, corporations, and hotel guests. The Wellness Walks became an educational tool to help more people discover the power of walking outside.

My walks also helped me discover the impact of nature indoors, biophilic design, and biophilia. Biophilia is our innate connection to the natural world. Psychoanalyst Erich Fromm coined the term in the early '60s, but it wasn't until the '80s that biologist E. O. Wilson popularized the concept. Since the industrial age, we have moved further and further away from nature— and we have become more and more unwell because of it. Nature has the answers; we just need to be present in it to receive the gifts. The podcast that I co-host, *Biophilic Solutions*, addresses the need to put nature first, and our guests share stories of how and why they are reconnecting people to the natural world through their work, products, and businesses. I am thankful that walking has opened the door to seeing the world through a beautiful new lens, one that is rich in nature, and to study the impact being outside has on all of us.

I am so happy you picked up this book. Walking has changed my life in such a profound and unexpected way. My walks have brought me such joy and delight and have helped me truly get to know the natural world in a way that I never thought possible. I hope you enjoy this book as much as I have enjoyed creating it just for you.

—Jennifer Walsh

PART ONE:
The Program

All About Stress

Yes, it can harm your health,
but you *can* do something about it.

Think of all the places you've walked so far this week. Not just the faraway places, but any place you used your feet to get to. You likely traversed the path from your bed to the kitchen, navigated from your front door to your car, and strolled down the produce aisle at your local supermarket. Whether long or short, walks are a part of our everyday lives—and they have the power to bring serenity and peace to our minds. However, you might be thinking the opposite is true for you. Maybe your mind begins broadcasting the day's to-do list as soon as you leave your bedroom, or your grocery run feels like an actual mental marathon spent worrying about money. We all too easily get caught up in the whirlwind of the day, but there is a way to actually transform all this rushing from place to place into a less stressful—and even calming—practice.

WHY YOU'RE FEELING MORE STRESSED THAN EVER

If you've noticed that you've been spending more time with your shoulders tensed up to your ears and your mind running through all the things you have to do, you're not alone. About 65% of women reported suffering from these symptoms daily, and 40% reported experiencing them multiple times a day, according to a 2019 *Prevention* survey conducted with the nonprofit HealthyWomen and health care communications agency GCI Health.

We're more stressed than ever, and it's coming from multiple angles. Of nearly a dozen choices in the above-mentioned survey, "family" and "household clutter or projects" were consistently the top two stressors across most demographics. (Women who worked were one exception—they rated "job demands" slightly higher.) This is a double whammy, because time at home and with family is when we're supposed to be relaxing and recharging.

One particular victim of this dynamic: our evenings. Normally, evening would be a time when, among other circadian changes, your body would be dialing back your cortisol levels to help you to unwind before bed. But in modern life, that's when women around the country are coming home, scrambling to put together dinner, looking around at a messy (or chaotic) living room, and thinking, "I can't deal." Human brains simply have to work harder to process jumble over order.

Aside from the endless list of to-dos, our environment also plays a role in how we feel. When we think about our disconnection from the natural world, it is profound. As of 2015, more than 50% of people lived in urban areas, and by 2050, this proportion is projected to be 70%, according to a study in *Proceedings of the National Academy of Sciences*. The study also noted what this increased urbanization might do to our overall mental well-being, and the outlook was, well, a little stressful. It linked city life with increased levels of mental illness, including anxiety disorders and depression. The authors noted that there are many potential causes for this relationship between urban dwelling and illness, which means you can certainly live anxiety-free in such an environment. However, the connection between densely packed, man-made environments and mental health issues is hard to ignore when you consider how much natural spaces do to ease anxiety and stress.

THE IMPACT OF STRESS AND ANXIETY

So, it's clear the modern world works in many ways to make us feel tense. And when life gets really busy, it's easy to accept a constant state of stress and anxiety as just part of the job. But being consistently wound up can have negative impacts on your health. Before we dive into all the wonderful things walking can do for you, let's take a quick look at what's going on in your body when those worrisome thoughts start rolling in. When we are frustrated or mad at ourselves for things we have done either an hour ago or 10 years ago, we are ruminating—that is, repeating and replaying not-so-happy thoughts. The subgenual prefrontal cortex, which is near the front of your brain, is responsible for those negative thoughts. Of course, stress and anxiety aren't always just about things that happened in the past. You might also worry about events and situations that haven't happened yet (and might never happen!). Either way, these feelings can manifest themselves as physical symptoms, like tension in your head, back, or shoulders, or in the ways listed below.

IT CAN CAUSE YOU TO MAKE BAD FOOD CHOICES.

When you're stressed, you're more likely to make unhealthy food choices and reach for bags of potato chips instead of carrot sticks. If you're under pressure, the adrenal glands produce cortisol, a.k.a. the stress hormone, while the brain has a low serotonin level. This induces cravings for comfort foods such as those high in simple carbohydrates. After you consume them, insulin levels in the blood increase and stimulate the brain to release stored serotonin. But this serotonin rush doesn't last long, and, soon after, you'll generally feel tired or hungry again and the same vicious cycle continues.

IT CAN INDUCE HEADACHES.

According to the Mayo Clinic, stress is the most commonly reported trigger for tension headaches. The pain is mild to moderate and can feel like a tight band around your head.

IT CAN INTERFERE WITH YOUR SLEEP HABITS.

There's a complicated relationship between stress and sleep. Basically, when you're pulling the string at both ends, you'll likely have trouble falling asleep or staying asleep because your mind is churning over negative thoughts.

IT CAN MAKE YOU MORE SUSCEPTIBLE TO ILLNESS.

Stress usually has a negative impact on sleep, diet, and exercise—all major components of overall health. So, it's no wonder that your immune system will also be compromised.

IT CAN MESS WITH GUT FUNCTION.

There's a strong connection between the brain and gut. When you're stressed, you're more likely to experience IBS symptoms such as diarrhea, an upset stomach, and bloating.

IT CAN ELEVATE YOUR BLOOD PRESSURE.

According to the American Heart Association, stress directly contributes to risk factors for high blood pressure—like a poor diet and excessive alcohol consumption—so, if you're stressed, your blood pressure is likely to go up.

IT CAN INCREASE YOUR RISK OF A HEART ATTACK OR STROKE.

It's not uncommon for people to suffer heart attacks or strokes when they are seriously stressed out. Stress stimulates a part of your brain called the hypothalamus, which in turn stimulates your adrenal glands to release the hormones cortisol and adrenaline. Your heart then has to hustle harder to keep blood flowing, causing fluctuations and elevations in blood pressure, and putting you at an increased risk of having a heart attack or stroke.

Stress and anxiety aren't pleasant experiences for your mind or body. And they can wreak havoc on both your long- and short-term health. Yet despite how truly painful it can be, when you are in the grip of stress and anxiety, you might feel helpless to do anything to alleviate them. You may feel too overwhelmed to try often-prescribed remedies like meditation or breathing exercises because you can't seem to focus your attention anywhere other than on your negative thoughts.

When you don't have the energy to engage in traditional calming practices, try something you've been doing since you were a small child: walking. That's it. You don't have to incorporate any special techniques or learn some complicated routine to start enjoying the soothing benefits of a short stroll. Walking is one of your greatest tools for dealing with stress. You can do it anywhere, any time, and you're probably already really good at it! Later on, you'll learn all about maximizing the calming power with tips and tricks, but you can start reaping the rewards right this moment by simply putting one foot in front of the other. And better yet, despite worry and stress's varied triggers (a heavy workload, caring for loved ones, trying to find time for your health), walking serves as a catchall solution to so many forms of stress.

The Power of Walking

Brighten your mood with every step.

So, what makes this humble mode of transportation so mighty? What is it about all forms of walking—even the hurried, going-to-miss-the-train kind— that is so beneficial to your brain? It's all about movement. The motion of moving forward allows oxygen and blood to flow through your body. The minute your feet hit the ground to start moving, it's almost like a rush of blood flow to the brain. Blood flow to your brain is important for all sorts of reasons. For one, it's how your brain gets the energy to perform vital functions. There are also the brain benefits you get from exercise in general. Research has shown that regular exercise can help alleviate depression and anxiety symptoms. That's because moving your body triggers the release of endorphins that simply make you feel good. It helps you to get unstuck from your thoughts. You don't need to lift weights or run a marathon to get those endorphins either. A gentle walk can be enough to completely change your mood. Those are just the benefits you get from walking anywhere—in your home, through the halls at work, or along the promenade at the mall. When you walk with other people (friends, family, coworkers), you get an added feel-good boost, because you're clocking quality time connecting with other people. And when you take your walks in nature, the happy vibes

person's daily routine. Never before has humanity been so far removed from nature. On your busiest days, your only breaths of fresh air might be the 40 feet from the parking lot to and from the entrance of your workplace. The impacts of living such a cooped-up life are varied, and that includes negative effects on your mental health. The resulting physiological condition even has a name, coined by author Richard Louv: nature-deficit disorder. Louv's 2005 book, *Last Child in the Woods*, explains the human connection to the natural world. In it, he cites a multitude of scientific research that suggests lack of time spent in nature is linked to a host of negative outcomes, including obesity, attention difficulties, and higher rates of physical illness. Physical detachment from forests, beaches, and parks may also cause an emotional detachment, as well, decreasing environmental stewardship. But it's the toll on our mental health, mainly higher rates of emotional illnesses, that seem most profound, as so many people struggle with stress, anxiety, and other conditions that impact everyday life.

increase even more. Plenty of studies show that a stroll in the great outdoors helps to decrease stress. For example, in 2015 Stanford University scientists found that when people took a quiet walk through a park, the part of the brain associated with fretting became significantly calmer and experienced less blood flow. Other research has shown that levels of serotonin, a neurotransmitter responsible for balancing mood, increase when you're exposed to sunlight. Sunshine also helps enhance vitamin D levels, which, when deficient, have been linked to depression.

The importance of time spent outside is magnified when you think about the typical

Although mental health issues are extraordinarily complex and many may not have a simple cure, the power of walking to help ease even a little bit of worry and woe is promising. Consider these other ways walking has been shown to calm the mind.

IT HELPS TO MINIMIZE DISTRACTIONS.
The old saying "out of sight, out of mind" has some truth to it. Walking in nature removes us from the worries of the inside world—

computers brimming with emails, rooms in need of tidying, and countless other things that might be weighing you down. Stepping outside creates breathing room between you and stressors, and it's in that space that you can find some peace. As you walk, your body and brain can move into a rhythm, allowing you to almost step outside all the open tabs in your mind and just be fully present. This cadence allows for the opportunity to witness the beauty that is around you.

IT HELPS YOU TO BECOME MORE MINDFUL.

Mindfulness, the practice of tuning fully into the present moment, has been shown to help alleviate stress and provide a sense of calm. It doesn't require you to empty your mind of thoughts, but rather to bring awareness to what's going on in your head and surroundings. Many mindfulness techniques rely on observing the rhythm of your breath, because it provides a steady and constant focal point for your attention. Think of it like this: It's much easier to focus on a single basketball directly in front of you than 14 basketballs bouncing in all directions. Your breath is the single ball. However, if you've ever had trouble sitting still and listening to your every inhale and exhale, you're not alone. Walking provides a more approachable—and just as powerful—alternative to traditional mindfulness exercises. That's because instead of focusing on the rhythm of your breath, you can focus on the rhythm of your footsteps. Bringing your attention to your stride acts as a cue to bring yourself back to the present, a.k.a. what is happening right now, and not what happened two days ago.

IT ACTIVATES YOUR SENSES.

There are also plenty of mindfulness techniques that center on engaging your senses—that is, identifying what you see, hear, smell, feel, and taste in a given moment. However, that's not always easy when you're stuck inside all day. So much of life is digital, meaning you lose the experience of seeing, smelling, and tasting that cupcake you just liked on Instagram. When you immerse yourself in a highly sensory experience, it is easier to pay attention to what you are hearing or seeing. Walking, specifically outdoors, provides that sensory experience. You can feel the crunch of gravel under your feet, see the sun shining on tree branches, smell the fresh-cut grass, hear the birds chirping, and maybe even taste the sweetness in the air. If you're walking on a beach, you can probably even taste the salty air on your tongue. These sensations are often so prominent, they're hard to ignore!

IT CAN HELP TO IMPROVE SLEEP.

You know a bad night's sleep can throw off your whole day and send your mind reeling. Luckily, walking outside can help get you on the right schedule. Natural sunlight plays a part in your circadian rhythm. Circadian rhythm is the natural, internal process, or clock, that regulates the sleep-wake cycle and repeats every 24 hours. Because we spend so much time indoors and out of natural sunlight, our circadian rhythm and sleep suffer. We are obsessed with sleep because we are getting so little of it. If we go for a walk first thing in the morning, the natural sunlight tells our bodies it is time to wake up. If you are struggling to sleep at night, it might actually be due to a lack of sunlight. Going for a short walk in the evening just after dinner also helps the body to sync into a nighttime state, helping to aid in preparation for a good night's sleep.

If you're not yet convinced of the awesome might of a simple stroll, consider the fact that some of the world's greatest thinkers, philosophers, and poets have been known for their love of walking. Steve Jobs attested that his greatest ideas came from his time spent walking, and he often would host walking meetings. Henry David Thoreau, the well-known naturalist, poet, and philosopher, dedicated an entire essay to the subject. In 1861, he published "Walking" and declared that every walk is a sort of crusade. Finally, the 19th-century German philosopher Friedrich Nietzsche might've put it best by saying, "All truly great thoughts are conceived while walking."

Walking offers so many benefits for your body and mind, and what makes it truly remarkable is just how easy it is to do. You can walk in any season and any weather (though I wouldn't suggest it in a blizzard or hurricane!). It can be done at any age, and it doesn't cost a penny. In your most frazzled moments, you can always get up and go for a walk. All you need to do is get moving, and in the following pages, I'll show you how to get the most out of every step.

How to Maximize The Calming Benefits of Walking

Quick and easy ways to get more out of your miles.

As you now know, there's some calming magic to be found in every step you take. But on those mad dashes to the train, you probably aren't feeling very relaxed. So, how do you tap into that power and make the most of it? There are some basic tips to help you think about the way you walk and move your body with each and every step that you take. Keep them in mind as you work your way through the 101 walks in this book and any walks thereafter. Let's get started on the road to feeling great with your map to new ways of walking into wellness.

FOCUS ON YOUR STEPS...

If you find it difficult to bring awareness to your breath, start by paying attention to your feet. Your stride provides a similar constant, reliable rhythm to your breath. No matter where you are on your walk, your footsteps

will be there for you to tune into. If they're not, you're not walking! Even if you're hurrying down the hall to a meeting or navigating a mall packed with holiday shoppers, you can dial into this sensation and bring yourself back to the present. Sometimes it's not as easy as "just pay attention," so think about these questions as you move to come to full awareness: What does it feel like as each foot hits the ground? What part connects with the earth first? How do your feet feel in your shoes? Observe these little details, and soon you will notice the unfailing rhythm. This awareness will bring you into mindfulness and all the positive, calming things that come with it.

...AND YOUR BREATH

Your breath is just as powerful a tool for engaging in mindfulness as your steps, so try thinking about the way you breathe. While it may sound simple, observing how you breathe

Walking Checklist

For a truly calming walk, you'll want to minimize the potential for any obstacles. Do these things before heading out to ensure everything goes smoothly.

☐ ### Check the weather.
Will you need multiple layers of clothing to protect you from the cold or moisture-wicking pieces that will help you to keep cool?

☐ ### Wear sun protection.
Whether you can see the sun or not, your skin is exposed to potential damage when you're outside. Apply sunscreen and consider wearing a hat and sunglasses.

☐ ### Choose comfortable shoes.
It sounds like a no-brainer, but what feels supportive enough for wearing to the office might leave you with blisters on a long walk. Factor in the weather and terrain to determine if you need hiking boots or if lightweight sneakers will do.

☐ ### Drink some water.
Dehydration impacts how your entire body functions, so if you aren't getting enough H_2O, it will impact your walk. Drink a glass before you leave, and consider bringing a bottle along if you're walking for an extended period of time or in severe heat or cold. There are a ton of lightweight and hands-free fanny pack options for stashing your water as you walk.

☐ ### Stretch.
Limbering up before you head out the door will help you to move more smoothly and avoid injury. This is not necessary for most walks, but it's worth stretching before covering a significant distance, walking on hilly or uneven terrain, or attempting the more physical walks in this book, such as the Walk-Run Walk on page 50.

Have fun with your walks, enjoy them, and know that every step you take is another step toward better health and well-being. Your body and brain are benefitting from your movement every single moment and every single day.

with each step—without trying to change it in any way—allows you to feel more present. And it's something you can easily return to at any point in your walk to bring your mind back to center. Your breath is one constant you can count on. You don't have to think about doing it for it to happen—it's just always happening in the background. When you pay attention to it, it comes into the foreground, along with every other amazing thing happening in the moment. The worry washes away.

Your breathing may fluctuate depending on what type of walk you do, but it will always help to bring you into a state of mindfulness. Tuning into this is especially impactful during a walk, because there is so much of which to be pleasantly aware. It gives you the opportunity to feel the places and spaces you're walking in just by activating your senses and allowing the environment in which you walk to be a part of your day. Just like anything, mindfulness takes practice, but it is a great tool that you can take with you through the rest of your life.

How to Use the 101 Walks

Take your first step to a calmer you.

Now that you know the basics of walking to reduce worry, you may be wondering why you need 101 different walks (or how there could possibly be that many different ways to walk!). Just like with any other endeavor, when you don't have a plan, it can be difficult to achieve your goals. These 101 exercises are intended to keep you engaged with your walking practice and turn it into an ongoing habit in your life. More than that, the walks selected for this book were designed as exercises in mindfulness to help you master the habit of getting out of your head and finding the calm of the present moment, no matter what is going on in your life. They use different techniques to help you dial into the present (like the one on page 60, which requires you to touch the trees and plants you encounter, or the Posture Walk on page 162, in which you'll tune into how you carry your shoulders, back, and head as you move). All of them require you to set out on your walk with intention instead of the typical rush from point A to point B. By the end of this book, that will be second nature to you.

Each walk is broken up into three parts: information on why the walk is valuable, how to best perform the walk, and a series of writing prompts. These prompts are intended to help you further zone in on what you saw, felt, and experienced during the walk. In the beginning, perhaps you will only be able to recall a few details of the walk. As you get better at paying attention to everything around you,

you will likely be able to fill pages with your observations! You can take this book with you and fill out the prompts along the way, or make a calming ritual out of it when you return and settle in with a cup of tea and your thoughts. Either way, review the questions before heading out so you can begin each walk with cues about what to pay attention to.

Not all of these walks are traditional. Some will ask you to simply observe what you see in nature, while others will ask you to skip and jump and be silly. You'll take walks in places you may have never been before and discover new ways to look at the routes you've taken a hundred times. Each has a suggested duration (feel free to go for shorter or longer), and they range from one minute to more than an hour. My intention is that each and every walk will show you all the good around you at any moment. Use this book as a guide to try new ways to walk and explore. You can use the walks as a way to not only get exercise, but also to witness things around you that you may have previously overlooked.

WHEN TO WALK

Try walking as often as possible. If you can only do it once a week for 15 to 20 minutes, that's a great start. Aim for three days a week for 20 minutes or longer, ideally outdoors. As you start walking more mindfully outside, you will discover just how far-reaching the benefits of nature are to your entire well-being. If you become an avid walker, like me, you may want

to begin walking every day. I also enjoy doing other workouts in addition to my daily walks, which you can try as well. Once you begin to see all that you can do while walking, you might want to do it more than you initially thought you would.

HOW TO PICK THE RIGHT WALK

No matter which of these walks you decide to do on a given day, you will end up feeling calmer than when you started. That being said, at times you may find yourself in the mood for some walks more than others. Feel free to do these walks in order, or jump around and find what speaks to you. When you return, write down all that you experienced during that walk. I also suggest writing down the date that you completed the walk. You might want to return to doing that walk again to see how you felt the previous time you did the walk versus how you felt or what you experienced on the latest one.

WHAT NOT TO DO

There aren't many rules for getting in a good, mood-boosting walk. You don't have to move at a specific speed or cover a certain distance, but you should avoid major distractions. Hold off on texting, talking to someone on the phone, or checking your email. You will, of course, still get the physical benefits of the walk, but your mind will be pulled out of the moment. Some of the 101 walks invite you to listen to music, but for the most part, stay unplugged.

You may also want to consider organizing a walking group. Not only will this help you to stay accountable for your regular walks, but it will also add a social dimension to your practice, which provides its own feel-good benefits. Enlist a friend (or five!) to join you at a regular time every week. Additionally, you can loop in family members and enjoy a different walk every week as a bonding opportunity. Work your way through this book together during the course of a year, and then look back on all you accomplished together. If you can't find any fellow walkers nearby, check out the range of apps that connect you with others to share your daily step count and chat about your walks. It'll add a little competitive element!

FINAL THOUGHTS

Be kind to yourself. If you don't get very far or if you are walking less than the prompts suggest you do, that is OK. The most important part is that you are doing it. You are trying and you are moving forward! Going for a short walk is better than no walk at all, even if you can just go outside for a 10-minute walk around the block. The gradual, gentle movement gets the blood and oxygen flowing. Like anything, you will build momentum, and this book will help you to get there. Have fun writing. Be elaborate. Be creative. Sketch your answers, press flowers between the pages, make it your own. Did something completely hilarious, outrageous, or unexpected happen on your walk? Write it down. This is your space to let worries go and just be.

PART TWO:
The Walks

Wellness
WALK

**This is a mindfulness walk,
one that is slow but intentional.**

Think of it like yoga for your brain. You'll tune into your body
with every step. This slow and deliberate walk will activate
the senses we often don't pay attention to when we are
indoors, like our sense of touch and smell. Most days we have
so many tabs open in our brains. This walk helps calm the
chaos and focuses your attention on one thing: the beauty of
nature around you. You'll naturally fall in step with the
present moment, bringing your brain into soft fascination
mode. In this mode, your brain is gently engaged, meaning
you're not expending a lot of energy and therefore you
become relaxed. Another benefit? This leisurely stroll can
help lower blood pressure.

15-20 MINUTES

HOW TO DO IT

To perform a Wellness Walk, spend at least 15 to 20 minutes (if you have more time, go for an hour or two) exploring a nature trail or even a city street with some greenery. Walk at a slow pace without headphones. Witness the plants, the trees, and the wildlife around you. Notice that your breath and steps become almost in tune with one another. Touch a tree and note what you feel.

What did you hear?

What did the air feel like on your skin?

Describe, in detail, what the tree you touched felt like.

Grounding
WALK

Grounding (or earthing) is the practice of allowing the energy of the earth to move through you by placing your bare feet directly on the natural ground.

Although it may seem a little unconventional, grounding is not a new concept. Research on its benefits is limited, but studies have linked this practice to better cardiovascular health, increased immunity, pain reduction, and mood improvement. Plus, it just feels good! Often we forget the true joy of really moving our toes—we're so used to having our feet so tightly squeezed into our shoes. Many shoe companies have tried to create shoes that mimic earthing or minimize the amount of material between your soles and the ground, but nothing beats the real thing!

10-15 MINUTES

HOW TO DO IT

On the next nice day (too cold and your feet will feel frozen!), go to a park, a beach, or somewhere you feel comfortable taking off your shoes and spending some time walking. You don't need to go far to receive the healing benefits of grounding. You can even pace in a backyard—speed and distance covered don't matter. The minute you step into the space to begin grounding, allow yourself to be fully present. Take in the sights, sounds, and scents all around you in the moment. Spread out your toes, wiggle them, let your feet fully grasp the soil beneath you. It's OK if your feet get dirty—that's even better. Walk slowly. Be aware of your posture. Feel the energy move through you with each step. Take a deep breath with each step, inhale and exhale.

How did it feel? On what surfaces did you walk? What was the temperature like on your feet?

What did you feel grateful for as you walked?

Where did you walk? What makes this location special?

Rain

WALK

"There is no such thing as bad weather, just bad clothes."

This is a phrase that is often used by the military, and couldn't be more true. So, embrace blustery weather and dress accordingly! The sights, sounds, and scents of a walk in the rain are often some of the most powerful for your senses. The colors of the ground, trees, plants, and leaves all become a new shade. The air smells fragrant and rich (depending on location and time of year). Once you begin a practice of walking in the rain, you will want to do it everywhere you go. The landscape takes on a new personality during rainfall, and to be fully aware, present, and in tune with it is a gift to your senses and your body.

5+ MINUTES

HOW TO DO IT

This is a time to channel your inner child! Don your favorite waterproof shoes or boots and grab your raincoat and umbrella, or put on a nice wide hat. Step out into the rain, walk at your own pace, and absorb this everyday phenomenon. This is not a timed walk; it is an opportunity to experience the beauty of the nature around you during a rainstorm. Please note: The rain walk is not recommended during a thunderstorm.

What did you hear?

What did you smell?

Did you carry an umbrella? What did the rain sound like as it hit the fabric?

Birding
WALK

Birding is one of the most accessible hobbies for people of all ages, no matter where you live.

What is birding? It is the simple act of walking through your neighborhood, local park, or anywhere you enjoy the outdoors to spot and identify local birds during different times of the year. It's a great opportunity to walk, explore, and direct your attention where you might not normally, like high up in tree branches. It's also a simple way to connect with family members both young and mature. Invite others to explore and find birds with you. You're sure to find that everyone quickly gets hooked. The more birds you see and hear, the more you'll want to know and the more you'll want to go outside and walk around to see what else you can discover.

10+ MINUTES

HOW TO DO IT

Put on comfortable shoes and grab your binoculars if you have them (but they're not necessary) to spot birdlife up close. Go to the nearest trees you can find, walking quietly and slowly. Look around at places birds commonly perch—tree branches, telephone lines, light posts, and bushes. Eventually you may be able to identify the birds by their sounds, so spend some time listening to the tunes they create. Photograph or journal about your new findings.

What time of year is it?
What did you see?

How many different types of birds did you see?

Have you ever seen them before? If so, where and when?

Constellation
WALK

Taking a stroll after the sun goes down can offer a totally fresh perspective.

After all, everything looks a little different in the moonlight. A constellation walk is a reminder to gaze up at the night sky and all the stars that fill it. You'll likely find it opens your eyes and mind to an unfathomable amount of beauty and wonder. There is so much more out there to see and understand and get to know better. The night sky continues to change as it gets later in the evening and also depending on where you are on the globe. The more you learn about the planets and stars, the more exciting it becomes to venture out and seek the bright lights up above.

10+ MINUTES

HOW TO DO IT

At dusk or later into the night, grab a flashlight (and binoculars, if you have some) and walk in your neighborhood to find a clearing away from streetlights. Go solo or invite a friend or family member. Either way, let your inner explorer come out. Pause every so often to take notes on what you see. Try repeating this walk at least once during each season to find different stars in the night sky. There are wonderful apps that help you find exactly where the stars are and when there might be meteor showers in your region. This isn't always easy to do for city dwellers, but it's great to try when you're away from the big city lights.

Did you find star formations that you haven't seen in a long time? How did it make you feel to see them?

Look for varying colors and brightness of stars. Did you see colors you weren't expecting? Were some much brighter than you thought?

Describe or draw the constellations you saw. Note the time of night and time of year.

Hiking

WALK

A hike is like any other walk but in a different landscape.

Instead of city skyscrapers or suburban homes, your path will be lined with towering trees or fields of grass. Most involve a series of inclines and declines. Some trails may be paved, but oftentimes they're quite rocky—and that's a good thing. The uneven, natural terrain forces your attention on the ground below. This continuous focus on your external surroundings helps you get out of your head, relaxing your prefrontal cortex. If you're visiting a town for the first time, hikes are a wonderful way to see the heights of that particular city and get in a solid workout.

30+ MINUTES

HOW TO DO IT

First, find a trail near you. You don't need to trek out to a national park—you might find some small hills in a wooded part of your neighborhood. Once you pick your path, grab the right shoes. You'll want footwear that supports your entire foot and suits the terrain on which you will be hiking. What you need on a hike in Florida in July will be very different from what you would need in Colorado in February, so get to know the climate you are in. Depending on location and what you are looking to accomplish, a hike can take 30 minutes or up to a few hours. No matter the distance, bring water so you stay hydrated. If you choose to hike in an unfamiliar location, it's best to go with another person or in a group. Get to know the conditions of that route before you head out. You'll want to determine how long the path might take so you don't end up hiking back in the dark.

What did the ground feel like under your feet?

How did the scenery change as you hiked? Did it become more wooded or open into a clearing?

Describe any wildlife you saw.

Power
WALK

Faster than the pace you might take to walk to your car, a power walk is all about getting your heart rate up.

By boosting your speed, you'll burn more calories than your typical stroll but you'll also get some calming benefits. The hasty pace causes your brain to release chemicals called endorphins that stimulate relaxation and improve mood. Plus, you'll get relaxation benefits from all the deep breathing. Because this walk is brisk, you will need good shoes to support your foot as you stride. For a little challenge, you might want to use an app to track your heart rate, pace, and mileage as you go.

20 MINUTES

HOW TO DO IT

Start at a pace somewhere between a really quick walk and a very slow run. Keep your back straight and avoid hunching forward. While walking, move your arms in rhythm with the movement of your feet, back and forth just like you would do during a regular walk, but faster. Your stride may feel awkward at first, but once you begin to work this into your routine, you will get the hang of it. If you have any knee or hip issues, be gentle. This pace might not be best for you, so feel free to just slow down and do what is truly best for your body and movement.

How did your body feel when you were moving it more quickly? Was anything tense?

Did you find a specific pace at which your body felt great? How did it compare to the feeling of running?

Did you listen to music or to the sounds around you? How did what you heard impact your movement?

Sunrise

WALK

Getting out of the house before dawn can seem daunting, but the beauty you will witness in a stunning sunrise—the colors, the hazy clouds—can set a positive tone for your whole day.

Starting your morning with some awe can leave you feeling more capable of handling the hours that follow. And the greatest joy is observing how every sunrise is different. That's the best gift of all. This walk is all about being present to drink in the sunrise, whether it comes with a rainbow or a little bit of rain.

20 MINUTES

HOW TO DO IT

The time the sun rises varies, of course, throughout the year and the world, so check the time of the next day's sunrise before going to bed. The sun rises in the east, so figure out which direction that is from your home, and start walking that way. Scope out viewpoints in your neighborhood to discover the best spot to watch the event, perhaps a hilltop or a bridge. This walk is not fast, so you can wear shoes or not. It truly depends on where you are.

What did you feel when you saw the sunrise? Did you feel at peace and at ease?

What was the weather like? What time of year is it?

How was this sunrise different from others you've seen?

Tiptoe
WALK

Can you remember the last time you tiptoed anywhere?

If not, today is a great day to try and do it again. Aside from being a delightful detour from your everyday routine, a tiptoe walk is a way to build or maintain strength in your feet and toes. It might feel silly, but moving your body in ways that you used to do as a child is important for getting your brain in play mode. Your feet are intended to be used in many ways, and tiptoeing helps with mobility and balance. Grab your family members and have them join the fun!

5+ MINUTES

HOW TO DO IT

This walk can be done in your home, your yard, a park, or anywhere you have outdoor space. Try it barefoot to allow your toes to do the work that they love to do. If that is not possible, put on your most comfortable shoes, such as walking or running sneakers. If you are barefoot, spread your toes out as you walk, letting each one almost grip the ground beneath you. If you are wearing shoes, don't worry about the sensorial feeling of gripping the ground below you. Walk slowly and allow your body to move differently than you usually do. Think of yourself as a ballerina, stretching your body higher. If you feel unstable, use a wall as your support as you walk. A few minutes is all you need to observe how this new way of moving feels.

How did your foot feel as you elongated it into this position?

How did your body try to find balance? Did you automatically stretch your arms up as if you were reaching something high in the air?

How did you breathe as you tiptoed?

Did you feel a smile on your face?

Silent

WALK

Music or conversation can be calming accompaniments to your strolls, but there is value in taking a silent walk every so often.

This walk is quiet. Leave your earbuds at home and put your phone on silent or vibrate mode. Instead, fully embrace being silent and dial into the sounds around you, from the rustle of the breeze to the sound of your own footsteps. We often rush from place to place and rarely allow ourselves to be silent. This is not a time to read emails on your phone. Give yourself permission to listen and hear the sounds around you, and that's it. We become more in tune with our bodies when we are silent and fully in listening mode. Our bodies are always speaking to us, but we rarely hear them because we are so busy speaking to others. When you listen, you can understand what your body needs to restore calm. This is a practice and something to get used to, especially if you tend to have a busy home or work schedule.

15+ MINUTES

HOW TO DO IT

Put on your comfortable shoes and head out the door. This walk can be in your neighborhood, a local park, or truly anywhere. Try it for just 15 minutes, or go longer at your own pace. Once you begin to tune in, you'll become aware of all the nuances that time of day offers by the sounds around you. The more you do this, the more you will get to know your neighborhood, the seasons, and even what time of day it is, all while being unplugged.

What did you hear when you took a silent walk?

Were you surprised by all that you heard around you? Why or why not?

How did you feel after the walk? Invigorated? Refreshed?

Hand-Weight

WALK

Get ready to work up a sweat!

If you don't want to stay indoors for a workout, grab your weights and go. On this walk you will build strength, muscle, and cardio endurance. Whether you pump the weights as you go or simply hold them at your sides, a sense of accomplishment should wash over you by the end—and perhaps a bit of gratitude, too, for the strength you have to carry these weights and walk freely.

20+ MINUTES

HOW TO DO IT

Put on your most comfortable walking or running shoes. Give yourself a few minutes to stretch your arms, legs, and the rest of your body. When you're ready to start walking, grab two weights (dumbbells or wrist weights are good options) that you would be comfortable carrying for 20 minutes or more. It might be one, two, or five pounds or more. If you don't feel comfortable carrying one in each hand, start with one weight in one hand and alternate between hands as you walk. Walk at your own pace and simply hold the weights as you go. If you feel comfortable enough, you can even begin lifting weights over your head and back down again as you walk for added strength training and coordination benefits.

What muscles did you feel engage as you walked with the weights?

Describe the path you walked.

How did your body feel with this movement? Did you feel confident and strong?

Beach

WALK

Whether you get to the beach once a day or once a year, that's enough time to feel the centering power of a stroll along the shoreline.

The beach provides a multisensory experience—the sound of the waves, the smell of the air, the feeling of the sand—that can help pull your mind away from worry and back to what is in front of you. The restorative feeling isn't in your head. Studies have shown that negative ions, which are electrically charged molecules floating in the air, can help decrease depression symptoms in some people. Negative ions are found in a variety of natural places, including the ocean. You'll also get a good workout. Your legs use different muscles to propel you through the sand than they would on pavement. And don't worry too much about the season. A winter walk by the ocean can be just as calming—just be sure to bundle up from head to toe!

10+ MINUTES

HOW TO DO IT

Kick off your shoes and let your feet sink into the sand. (If the weather is cold, keep your shoes on so you stay warm and comfortable.) As the sand shifts beneath you, your feet will move in ways that they usually don't. Be mindful of the sensation beneath your soles. Start walking at your own pace. Take a deep breath, and inhale and exhale. Continue walking in this way for as long as you like. Pick up some of the rocks, shells, or other natural elements that have washed up on shore. If you want more of a workout, walk on the softest sand you can find, so your feet sink in as you go. You'll use more muscle power with each step.

How did the sand between your toes feel?

What did the air smell like? Could you almost taste the saltiness? How did it make you feel?

Did walking on the beach bring back any memories?

What shells, rocks, or other natural elements did you find? What did they feel like in your hands?

Walk-Run

WALK

If you don't like the idea of adding running to your walks, don't worry.

You won't run for more than a minute straight during this energizing routine. The Walk-Run Walk is intended to raise your heart rate and get your blood flowing by alternating between a normal-paced walk and a quick jog. Varying your pace will keep you engaged with your route the entire time. You'll also build endurance for longer walks (and even runs!). You might want to use the stopwatch on your phone to remind yourself when to start and stop running, but you can also estimate 1 minute by identifying a tree or house in the distance and jogging until you reach it. Bonus: Looking in the distance benefits your eyesight as well. For millennia, humans spent a lot of time looking in the distance searching for food or watching out for predators, but we do so less often in the era of the smartphone. This walk is an easy way to give your eyes a break!

15-20 MINUTES

HOW TO DO IT

This walk is best performed in less-crowded areas or anywhere you have plenty of space to walk and run. Start by lacing up your running shoes and stretching any body part that feels tight. Head out the door, and walk for 5 minutes or so to loosen up your body, then set your stopwatch for 1 minute and run. After 1 minute, walk again for 3 to 4 minutes, then run again for 1 minute. Repeat this for 15 to 20 minutes. Don't forget to take good, deep breaths along the way and to do some stretching when you are finished.

How did your body feel after each short burst of running?

How did your body feel after the entire walk-run was over?

Where did your thoughts go as you ran?

I Spy
WALK

Have a lot on your mind? Let's go for an I Spy Walk.

Often, we have so much running through our heads that we can't think straight. The simplest remedy: Go for a walk and look around. It might seem childlike (and it is, but we need a dose of that on occasion!), but it is also great for your brain to reshuffle from thinking about to-do lists or worst-case scenarios and instead zone in on a single, achievable task. When your brain stops overprocessing thoughts and focuses on one thing at a time (like what you see in front of you), your mind calms down. It relaxes its grip on everything else. This walk is especially fun with a partner, so enlist a friend or invite your children to join in the fun!

10+ MINUTES

HOW TO DO IT

No matter the weather, go out and really look at what's in front of you. What do you spy? Repeat what you find in your head or share it with your walking partner. I spy a new neighbor; I spy a red car; I spy a tree in bloom.

Did you feel relaxed after you walked for a few minutes?

Did you realize that you were no longer bogged down by so many thoughts?

Did you have a smile on your face playing I Spy like you did as a child?

Pet

WALK

Time spent with pets in general has been shown to be calming.

According to research, pet owners—especially dog owners—have lower blood pressure than non-pet owners. This is mostly because dog owners often spend more time walking, and also because petting an animal can help put you into relaxation mode. You can get even more calming benefits by engaging in a mindful walk with your pet. When you set out for your walk with the intention of being present, you might notice and appreciate things you didn't observe before. This activity works for any type of pet you might walk with: dogs, cats, rabbits, and even a bird on the shoulder or a horse on the farm. Bonding with an animal while walking is incredibly good for your innate connection to the animal kingdom. Plus, it's a chance for you and your pet to get outside and move your bodies together.

10+ MINUTES
HOW TO DO IT

You can make this type of walk anything you would like it to be. Maybe you have a new dog and you are getting to know one another so you are on a learning walk. Maybe this is your longtime companion that is always up for a nice long walk. If you have a younger pet, this is an opportunity to be mindful of the fact that they are looking for direction from you on what to do or how to behave. It's time to take the lead, quite literally, and teach your new companion the way to walk. You just might learn something along the way too!

How did your pet act on this walk? Did their personality come out?

Did you notice your pet always wanting to go in a certain direction or to a particular place?

When did your pet get the most excited?

Scent
WALK

Sometimes being mindful of everything our senses are exposed to at once can feel overwhelming.

Isolating a single experience, like what you are smelling, is a great way to re-center. A Scent Walk helps you do just that. And with all our rushing from place to place enclosed in cars and buses and planes, we don't always get a chance to truly stop and smell the roses. We're often indoors and cut off from the scents of the natural world—freshly cut grass, midsummer rain, crisp fall leaves. Once you begin to tune into the scents around your neighborhood, you will begin to understand what time of year different smells occur, like when the lavender blooms. And you're not limited to the scents of nature. Maybe your local restaurant makes the best Italian food, and every time you walk by you inhale the smell of their garlic dishes. It's all worth soaking in!

15+ MINUTES

HOW TO DO IT

Set out for a walk like you typically would, and move at your own pace. As you start walking, take a deep breath through your nose. What do you smell? Really think about the time of year, as this can help you identify the aromas around you.
If you're walking during the colder months, do you smell the wood burning in a fireplace? If you're out in the summer beside the ocean, maybe you can smell the salt air. It's OK if you don't smell anything in particular—perhaps there is no specific scent. Just keep your attention tuned into your sense of smell.

When you began walking, were you surprised by all that you smelled on your walk?

<u>Did any of the scents prompt fond memories?</u>

<u>Did you feel encouraged to take this walk again soon?</u>

Walking
MEETING

Want to get colleagues to think outside the box?

Go for a Walking Meeting. If you can't be together side by side, take your work calls outside for a walk. President Barack Obama was known for his walking meetings at and around the White House when he was in office. More and more people are opting to take the team for a walk around the property, to a local park, or even just around the perimeter of the office. We are more creative and prone to think bigger and more unconventionally when we are outdoors.

15+ MINUTES

HOW TO DO IT

Ask your team or colleagues to either bring a comfortable pair of shoes to work or always keep a pair handy to rise to the occasion and get to stepping. It's also a collaborative way to get the team's steps in. People feel invigorated and optimistic when a walk is offered versus sitting around the table in a conference room.

Did the discussions feel more lively while you were walking?

Did the walk and talk feel inspirational and motivational?

What was the weather like?

Did the walk lift your mood and get you excited about next steps that were discussed during your walk?

Bark

WALK

Nope, this one has nothing to do with a dog.

This walk is actually about getting to know your neighborhood trees better. Taking a closer look at a tree's bark can help you identify the type of tree it is and give you a better understanding of the biodiversity in your community. You might also find a deeper appreciation for all that these mighty plants do, such as providing a canopy of green leaves in the peak of summer to keep you cool as you walk beneath them.

10+ MINUTES

HOW TO DO IT

Seek out a path with plenty of trees. Stop and observe the bark of a tree. Feel it, and note its incredible texture. Tune in with your other senses. Repeat this walk throughout the year, and take note of how the bark looks in the rain, snow, or other elements. If you're feeling creative, make a bark rubbing by placing a piece of paper over the bark and lightly coloring the paper with pencils to create an imprint of the bark.

What was the bark of the trees like? Did the bark shed like birch trees?

Did the bark have any specific scent?

What did the tree's height or width indicate about its age?

Treadmill
WALK

The great outdoors isn't the only place to enjoy the benefits of walking.

A treadmill at home or at your local gym offers a way to get your steps in when weather conditions are less than ideal for a stroll outside. Although your scenery won't change as you're pacing the treadmill, there are plenty of ways to keep your mind engaged and calm on an indoor walk. You can adjust the incline to really get your heart pumping. And you never have to worry about ending up too far from home!

20+ MINUTES

HOW TO DO IT

Before you get on the treadmill, do a few stretches to warm up. Once on the machine, start walking and play around with your pace until you find what's comfortable for you. If you're looking to truly maximize this walk, go for 30 to 45 minutes and alternate your pace between a fast walk and a slower one. For more of a challenge, add an incline to your fast walk, then go downhill and slow down slightly. Play some music to keep yourself moving. You can eventually incorporate light hand weights or dumbbells (two or five pounds). Try doing arm lifts with the weights to get your whole body activated.

How did your body feel going faster and slower?

Did you feel out of breath when you were trying to move uphill?

What differences did you notice in your body and mind between walking on a treadmill and walking outside?

Exploration

WALK

When was the last time you went out to explore?

Sure, everything may seem to have already been discovered and documented on Google Maps, but surely there are paths you haven't yet walked in your own neighborhood, local park, or even a favorite national park. Perhaps it's a side street you never go down or an entrance to the park you never use. You'll likely find things you never knew were there. An Exploration Walk is an opportunity to really open your eyes and witness what's happening around you. You'll notice even more if you repeat this walk throughout the year. A lush green landscape in the summer may reveal itself to be something entirely new in the barren months of winter.

5+ MINUTES

HOW TO DO IT

Explore for as long as you find it interesting, but give yourself at least 5 minutes to really get into it! Don't worry about getting your heart rate up, just step out and start wandering. You can head out on your typical neighborhood walking route and keep your eyes open for new paths or streets to traverse. To ensure you don't roam too far off the beaten trail, you might want to use your smartphone's map app to help you get back.

What did you discover? Were you surprised by what you found? Note what season it is.

Describe any new sensory experiences you found. Did you come across new scents or sounds?

Main Street
WALK

It doesn't matter if you have an actual Main Street, or if you just walk along a street with many local shops, restaurants, and galleries.

What better way is there to get to know your locale than to walk your local shopping and dining district? This is a great weekend walk to explore what might be new in the neighborhood. You might meet new business owners or neighbors, stumble across a coffee shop you didn't know about, or find a serene bench for taking a break and writing in this book! You'll only grow closer to your city and, who knows, you may even find ways to make it better (that vacant lot could be the perfect spot for a community garden).

1-2 HOURS

HOW TO DO IT

Pick a weekend or time when you have an hour or even a few hours to walk and see what is going on. You can even plan a walking tour with friends as a way to shake up your regular routine. Don't be afraid to act like a tourist and look up! Admire the architecture, murals, and little details that make this environment unique.

Describe one new place or space on your Main Street Walk you saw that you didn't know existed.

What was the atmosphere like? Was it lively? Was there a lot of traffic?

What were you most surprised about during this walk?

Crab
WALK

In need of a reminder to take things a little less seriously?

Engage in a couple minutes of this playful exercise from your childhood. Mimicking the movement of a crab, this type of walk will move your body not only in new ways, but in ways that help you grow stronger. We are so used to sitting all day and moving in a limited number of positions, but it is essential to be able to function in a whole range of movement. The crab walk will shake you out of your routine and, perhaps, get you back to that carefree mindset you had as a child.

1-2 MINUTES

HOW TO DO IT

Find an area with plenty of space and kick off your shoes so you are completely in touch with the ground below your feet. Squat down and sink your butt as close to the ground as possible, allowing your hands to touch the ground for balance if you need to. Begin squat-walking sideways or forwards and backwards. It might feel funny, but that's kind of the point! If you have any problems with your knees or hips, please consult with your doctor before trying this exercise.

Did you smile when you tried this? Did you envision a crab walking sideways?

How did your limbs feel as you did this? Did you fully feel your feet on the ground?

Did walking like this stir up a childhood memory for you? What were you doing and who were you with?

Snow
WALK

When a wintry day arrives, it's tempting to hunker down and watch the weather through your window.

But a walk in the snow is a rare opportunity to see your neighborhood in a completely different way. It allows you to experience the sheer beauty of nature because everything man-made is covered by powder. A snow walk is also an incredible workout. The deeper the snow, the more your body has to work to lift your heavy boots up with every step.

15+ MINUTES

HOW TO DO IT

First, bundle up in the proper gear to protect yourself from the cold and to prevent slipping on unshoveled paths. Having cold or wet feet really deters from a great Snow Walk experience. Once outside, take a moment to observe what you hear, see, feel, smell, and taste—from the sound of the snow under your boots to the scent in the air. Notice the snow on tree branches, rooftops, and fences. Walk for as long as you like.

Could you almost taste the air? If it was snowing, did you put out your tongue to catch the snowflakes?

What did your body feel like while you were walking? Were you exhilarated?

What did you hear as you walked?

What did you see as you walked?

Stroller

Have a little one in a stroller? WALK

Head out for a just-because walk, and show your children the magic of walking for joy, not just to get from place to place. If your child is old enough, you can even turn this into a learning walk by pointing out new things together, such as trees, plants, flowers, animals, or unique sites. Let this be a time to simply bond and walk. If you're needing more steps in your workout, don't ever underestimate the steps you can get in with a nice, long Stroller Walk.

10+ MINUTES

HOW TO DO IT

Pull on your walking shoes, grab the stroller, and get moving. This doesn't have to be a timed walk; it's more of a walk for enjoyment. If you do intend to walk for a while, don't forget to pack something to drink for yourself and the kiddos.

How did you feel strolling together?

What did your child seem most excited to see?

Was there a moment that grabbed your attention as well as your child's?

Nourishing WALK

Often we grab our car keys or hop on public transportation to go to a restaurant.

A walking tour of local eateries is a great way to experience the neighborhood and support your community businesses. You might strike up a conversation with the owners or meet some new people. Plus, post-meal body movement has been shown to help improve digestion—so a stroll around the block might be just the thing you need after a hearty meal!

1-2 HOURS

HOW TO DO IT

This walk is perfect for groups, so gather some friends, and pick three to four restaurants that are in walking proximity to each other. Go to one for appetizers, one for an entrée, one for dessert, and one for drinks. The break between each course will help you savor every bite. On your walk to each restaurant, take your time and enjoy your surroundings.

Did you find restaurants you weren't aware of or new things about places you've already been?

Did you wind up meeting the waitstaff or owners of the restaurants as you went along?

Was it a fun day with friends and family or did you try and venture out on your own?

Museum

WALK

Brain scans reveal that when we view art of any kind, it increases blood flow to the brain by as much as 10%—the equivalent of looking at someone you love.

Pair that with the power of walking and you've got a double dose of feel-good benefits. This combination of creativity and movement makes museums ideal environments for a good walk. You'll discover new artists, learn some history, and cover a lot of ground—likely without realizing it!

10+ MINUTES

HOW TO DO IT

This walk works for big or small museums. If the one you're visiting is large, grab a map before exploring. Going with others can be a fun way to get their take on art or the history of pieces you see. Make sure you set aside enough time to see everything on your list, and get to know the museum before going so you can find out if you need to purchase tickets in advance or anything else that is pertinent.

What were you surprised to see?

Describe what it was like inside the museum, from the feeling of the air to the sounds you heard.

Did this walk make you want to visit more museums?

Gratitude
WALK

A Gratitude Walk is one in which you are fully present and thankful for each step and moment just as it is.

It is so easy to sit and stew and fall into a pattern of negative thinking. So get moving! Nothing can change your perspective like quite literally changing your scenery and walking. When we fill our hearts and minds with gratitude, we are able to move to a better place of love, empathy, and kindness for ourselves and for others. Gratitude allows us to open our hearts to the beauty that is given to us. When we can walk in gratitude, we are more open to being hopeful for the future.

5+ MINUTES

HOW TO DO IT

This walk is great to do any time of day but can be especially powerful when done first thing in the morning. Enter this walk with a feeling of thankfulness for the day, no matter what the weather is like or the current situation you might be in. As you walk, name one thing for which you are grateful. It could be as simple as receiving a phone call from a loved one or enjoying hot coffee. Continue thinking of things you're grateful for with every couple of steps. Draw on your surroundings for inspiration (the community garden, a neighbor's setup, or a festive wreath on a front door).

Did this walk bring a smile to your face?

List five things you're grateful for that you thought about on your walk.

Were you able to find yourself fully present in the moment?

Mall

WALK

There are few places with as many flat, covered walking paths as your local mall.

Depending on the size of the mall, you can often quickly cover two to three miles before you even know it! Plus, with nearly all the amenities of home (restrooms, food, benches), these indoor shopping oases make for an ideal walking route on stormy days. Aside from getting in your steps, you may also find yourself absorbed in the sights, sounds, and smells. Some malls have even incorporated fun walking maps of things to see or experience on your strolls.

10+ MINUTES

HOW TO DO IT

These are great walks to do alone, with loved ones, or—if you have little ones—even young mom groups with strollers. Keep the momentum going by spotting new things on each lap. During one lap, look to see what store windows are the most intriguing to you. On the next lap, notice which stores have the best aromas. Finish off with a lap to see who has the best sales.

Were you surprised by what you actually discovered walking at the mall?

Did you see things you weren't expecting?

Did you enjoy going alone or with a group?

Botanical Garden

WALK

Botanical gardens are a wonderful place to experience the beauty of plant life while walking.

They often feature more elaborate displays than a typical garden you might find in your neighborhood, and they usually house a wide variety of plants and flowers. Plus, botanical gardens typically provide educational information, meaning you might just leave with a little more knowledge! Because these gardens are so immersive, you'll likely find it very easy to connect with nature and just unwind.

1+ HOURS

HOW TO DO IT

Find a botanical garden in your area and check their events calendar for any interesting exhibits. Consider bringing a camera to document the unusual blooms you find. As you walk, inhale all the floral scents. If you are allowed to touch the plants, definitely do so. You might be surprised that some feel different than you would expect!

What kinds of plants or tree life did you wind up seeing?

Was the garden indoors or outdoors? How did it feel when you walked?

Were there certain scents that you really liked? What were they?

Trash
WALK

Formally known as plogging, the act of walking, hiking, or running while picking up trash is a creative way to help out your community while getting in your steps.

You can easily turn any walk into a Trash Walk, but consider enlisting a group of friends or community members, and challenge everyone to pick up as much trash as possible. It's a no-pressure bonding experience and has an immediate impact on the environment around you.

30 MINUTES

HOW TO DO IT

Start by picking a street, park, or beach to clean up.
Equip everyone with gloves, multiple trash bags, hand sanitizer, and other tools as needed. You might be surprised at how quickly your efforts make a difference.

How many bags of trash did you fill up on your walk?

How did what you collected on this walk make you feel?

Did this walk make you think differently about what you consume every day?

Fresh-Cut Grass

WALK

Next time mowing the lawn feels like a chore, consider this mindful walk to help you see the bright side.

The fresh and earthy scent of grass is extra-strong right after it's been cut, so there is no better time to walk through it than when it's bursting with fragrance. It's almost like a childhood memory that washes over you. You likely walk through cut grass often, but doing it with the intention of paying close attention to its scent, feeling, and vibrant shade of green can result in a totally new experience.

↓

5+ MINUTES

HOW TO DO IT

First, find some fresh-cut grass! If you don't have a lawn, scope out local green spaces, like parks and fields. If you can, take off your shoes. Move your toes around in the grass, then begin walking slowly. Inhale all the bright green fragrance around you. You don't have to walk far; you can even just pace your yard if space is limited. If you have young children, nieces, nephews, or grandchildren, take them out in the grass and explore. These memories, often associated with scent, can last a lifetime. After you've walked a bit, don't forget the fun of also lying in the grass and searching the sky for clouds shaped like animals.

Did the scent spark a childhood memory?

Did you walk in the grass barefoot? How did you feel?

Did you feel the sun on your skin? Was it hot or cool out?

Roots
WALK

When was the last time you were in the neighborhood you grew up in?

Are you still close to where you were raised or are you now far away? If you're ever able to do a real Roots Walk, it is such a great way to reflect on where you came from.

10+ MINUTES

HOW TO DO IT

There are several ways to do a Roots Walk. You can visit the street you grew up on. Or, you can do a walk of your own personal lineage. Where were your grandparents and parents born and raised? Can you do a walk with them so they can point out places and moments in time that were meaningful to them? If you can, don't forget to take notes or maybe even video on your phone to document so you have those memories recorded.

Where did you go? What has changed since you last saw this neighborhood?

What did you learn or see for the first time?

Did you enjoy seeing the old neighborhood with new eyes?

What surprised you on this walk?

Track
WALK

Whatever your feelings about track were in high school, there's good reason to head back to the loop.

Doing laps around your local track is a great way to get in steps and change up your walking routine. Because you'll be walking in a loop, you can cover vast distances without ever heading too far from your car. This can make it less daunting to attempt longer distances than you have before.

15+ MINUTES

HOW TO DO IT

To keep your laps from feeling monotonous, you might want to listen to music or a podcast. When you walk, also notice what is outside of the track area. Do you see birds or other wildlife? Give yourself a goal—it doesn't have to be big. Maybe you want to walk a mile or two or just a few laps. Feel free to stroll leisurely or turn this into training for something bigger, like a 5K walk. If you are prepping for a walkathon or other event, bring a friend to help keep you motivated!

What did the weather feel like as you walked?

Did you walk farther than you initially expected?

Did walking the track remind you of your days at school? What did you think about?

Will you grab a friend to go with you next time?

Water
WALK

Do you live close to an indoor or outdoor pool?

Are you near a lake or even an ocean? Time to get on your bathing suit and start walking (yes, walking not swimming). This might not feel like much, but during a water walk you are moving your body in a way that it is not used to, and therefore you will be working different muscle groups. There isn't as much pressure on your body when walking in the water as there is on the pavement, so this is an ideal activity for those who need something soft on the joints. And, of course, it's a refreshing way of keeping cool!

10+ MINUTES

HOW TO DO IT

Water walks are best performed in water that is no higher than waist to chest deep. Feel free to start in the shallow end for a few laps, then gradually go a little deeper. The deeper the water, the more resistance you will feel and the more your muscles will have to work. If you want to walk in an ocean or lake but don't like the feeling beneath your feet, purchase water shoes, which will protect your feet. As you walk, use your arms to help you push the water behind you. The water will act as resistance. This will help you build lean muscle. Test out walking with big strides and little strides, but don't stress about form. The best way to get the most out of this walk is to just try it.

Was the water refreshing?

Were you surprised how great of a low-impact workout it was?

Are you looking forward to doing it again?

Spirit

WALK

Thich Nhat Hanh, the renowned Zen monk, author, and meditation master, teaches people to walk as a part of their spiritual practice.

The same has been true for people of all religions for millennia. For many, the link between walking and worshipping comes from the act of getting close to nature—and therefore a higher power—during an outdoor stroll. Whether or not you are religious, you can use this type of walk to find gratitude for the natural world.

15+ MINUTES

HOW TO DO IT

Try this walk in your favorite natural setting. Start by focusing on your breath and your footsteps as you walk so you can settle into mindfulness. Then you can begin to pray, repeat affirmations, or simply think about a few things for which you are grateful. If you have affirmations, consider writing them down and taking them with you for reference on your walk. There is no wrong way to do a spirit walk.

How long did you walk?

Was it reflective and also observational?

What did the air feel like on your skin?

What did you find yourself connecting to on this walk?

Touch
WALK

Often when we are out walking or hiking, we forget to touch the beauty of nature that is present all around us.

We have become so insular in our homes and offices that we have forgotten what it is to be childlike, to touch and explore the living things around us, to feel how connected we are. When we touch more living things, like microorganisms, every day, it helps build our immune systems. Ancient bacteria lives in the dirt around us. This bacteria has been linked to decreased inflammation and lower stress levels. And all you have to do to reap these benefits is touch it.

10+ MINUTES

HOW TO DO IT

You can do a Touch Walk anywhere you are. Are you walking down a street in a friend's neighborhood? Reach up and touch that leaf that is hanging above you. Are you on vacation and seeing brand-new vegetation you have never seen before? Have you ever felt a peeling birch tree? Whatever you are reaching for, be sure to first touch it gently. Not only will this help you slow down and process what you are experiencing, but it will also prevent you from grabbing a handful of prickly leaves or other dangerous vegetation.

Did you go alone or with family members?

What did you learn on your Touch Walk?

What did you feel?

What was your favorite thing that you felt on this walk?

Awe
WALK

Awe is a powerful emotion that is most often experienced when walking in nature.

It's more than acknowledging natural beauty; it's about being completely and unexpectedly overcome by its immensity and power. You don't need to visit the Grand Canyon to feel it. An Awe Walk can bring your attention to the magic of your local surroundings, from butterflies to a tree in full bloom. If you go for a walk to seek beauty, you will often find beauty no matter where you are. And if your heart, eyes, and mind are open to witnessing the beauty that is presented to you, then you are more apt to feel and experience awe. Think of the last time you saw a rainbow. What did you say to yourself when you saw it? Was it, "Wow, look at that beautiful rainbow?" That's awe. Awe helps calm the cerebral cortex and the mind. A sense of joy comes over your body.

5+ MINUTES

HOW TO DO IT

You don't have to go far to experience awe, but it will help you shift your brain into a more relaxed state of being. To keep your mind open to all awe possibilities, disconnect from your devices for this one. Awe can happen at any time, but sunrise and sunset are often ripe with opportunities. Ultimately, this walk is all about being aware of your surroundings, so look around you. What are you sensing? Maybe a certain scent will stop you in your tracks and make you think, "Wow, that is a breathtaking scent," or maybe it'll remind you of a special moment from your past.

What was it that prompted awe?

Was it day or night? Describe the time of day.

Did experiencing awe bring peace to your mind and body?

Music

WALK

The perfect soundtrack can completely change your mood and your pace.

Today, play with the power of music and listen to your favorite songs while you walk. On days when your mind is racing, a melody and lyrics can pull you back to the present. You might notice your steps begin to align with the beat, and that's great! Often music can inspire us to keep moving—and then we realize we have to walk all the back, too. So pay attention to the time of day and make sure you'll have enough light for the full journey. Maybe play music that you wouldn't normally listen to. Do you go for one genre of music like pop? How about giving classical a try? Remember this is a walk that will motivate you to keep going, so you might walk for 20 minutes or an hour.

10+ MINUTES

HOW TO DO IT

Prep a few walking playlists before you go—perhaps one with fast-paced songs and one with slower-paced songs. Music walks are best done where you have some room to groove, so look for a dedicated walking path, a park perimeter, or even the beach. Let your music choice determine how quickly and slowly you move your body forward. As you get into the music, feel free to let the rest of your body get into it by walking at a faster pace than you planned. Some songs can do that!

What kind of music really made you move?

Did you choose slower or more upbeat music? Why?

Did you walk farther than you thought you would?

Amusement Park

WALK

Perhaps you recall visiting a theme park or carnival when you were a kid and running from attraction to attraction with excitement.

This walk is a chance to slow down and absorb the thrilling sights and sounds of an amusement park—the whir of a roller coaster, the scent of funnel cake. You might also be surprised at how many steps you can get in. Many parks and state fairs take up large areas of land and have plenty of winding pathways to cover, but this walk works for any size park. If you have little ones, this is a good way to help tucker them out for a solid night of sleep afterwards!

1+ HOURS

HOW TO DO IT

Amusement park walks are great to do with family, but it can also be a long day, so go prepared. You might be able to bring your own drinks and snacks, but always check the rules before you go. Also, make sure everyone is dressed for the weather, and wear proper hats and sunscreen if you will be out in the sun all day. We often visit amusement parks hopping from one ride to another, but don't forget the experience of everything else around you—the sights, the scents, and even the people. There may even be flowers and trees in the park that you never noticed.

Where did you go?

List the most memorable thing you saw, heard, smelled, tasted, and felt at the park.

Did you ever think about how much you are actually walking at an amusement park?

Photography

WALK

During your next outing, set out with the intention of capturing what you see in photos.

It's a great way to move your body while getting creative. Walking with the purpose of finding things to photograph will push you to look more intently at everything around you. You might realize that the flowers that you always see from above would photograph beautifully from a vantage point in which you can see the undersides of the petals. Experiment with time of day and time of year. The sunlight will look different on houses, buildings, or trees as the day progresses. The landscape is always ebbing and flowing with the seasons, which means you are able to continually photograph new sights. By the end, you will have a one-of-a-kind photo essay of your walk.

15+ MINUTES

HOW TO DO IT

There is no wrong way to do a Photography Walk. Capture what inspires you, big or small. Don't stress about technical details, like composition or lighting—just snap away. If you'd like, pick a theme for each walk. Consider photographing just green things on one, perhaps just tree roots on another. Enlist family and friends, and compare your photo essays afterward to see how everyone experienced the walk differently.

What did you love to photograph?

What time of year did you go? What did the environment look and feel like?

Did you photograph people, buildings, or nature?

Breath

WALK

This may sound simple, but it is often overlooked.

When we walk, we are usually strictly focused on getting from point A to point B and don't stop to think about how we are breathing. After all, we don't need to think about breathing to do it. But when we tune into each inhale and exhale with every step, we can help release negativity from our minds and instead live in the present moment. The more you do this, the more aware you become of how you are breathing, whether it is fast or slow. This is a very calming walk and is helpful for relieving anxiety.

5+ MINUTES

HOW TO DO IT

Pick a quiet nature path for this one, and put your phone in silent mode. You'll want to be able to hear and feel your own breath without the distraction of busy streets or music. Walk slowly and begin taking deep slow breaths. Inhale for four seconds, then gently release that breath for four seconds. Do this sporadically during your walk to truly bring awareness to your breathing and to bring a sense of relaxation to the body as you continue to walk. If you find it difficult to pay attention, tune into the feeling of your chest rising and falling as you breathe. You might find that your breath begins to align with your footsteps. This walk works well in conjunction with other walks in this book, especially the Grounding Walk on page 24.

**Where did you feel your breath?
In your chest or maybe in your belly?**

How did it make you feel?

Were you surprised at how calming this was to do?

Mentor WALK

Have you ever noticed that deep and meaningful conversations just happen to unfold more easily on a walk?

And even more so when walking in nature? Take advantage of this comfortable setting, and invite your mentor or mentee on a short stroll. If you're not in a mentorship, suggest a walking meeting with someone you think would be a good fit. You'll likely find your discussion leads to more clarity and more shared information. Research has shown a direct correlation between walking and the free flow of ideas, so this is an ideal setting for exploring new concepts.

30 MINUTES-1 HOUR

HOW TO DO IT

Give yourself a decent amount of time for this walk so your conversation can flow naturally. You might be amazed at everything you end up talking about in just one hour. Bring a notepad and pen to jot down ideas and thoughts that arise.

Where did you wind up taking your Mentor Walk?

What was the weather like?

Did you feel inspired for next steps you are supposed to take?

State Park

WALK

There are thousands of state parks across America, and each one provides a unique snapshot of local ecosystems.

You'll discover the animals, trees, flowers, and landmarks that have existed in your state for centuries. These natural spaces are ideal for walking thanks to established trails and plenty of ambling fields. Wherever you roam, you'll get the calming benefits of fresh air and wide open spaces.

1+ HOURS

HOW TO DO IT

Research nearby state parks and pick a trail based on your skill level (some are more treacherous than others). You'll likely need hiking boots to support your feet on uneven terrain. Give yourself at least an hour to perform this walk so you have plenty of time for unexpected exploration. Unlike a walk through your neighborhood, a state park walk allows you to experience the profound beauty of nature untouched by human development. The park might have unique wildlife, rock formations, trees, or historic structures within its borders that make it unique to that region, so keep your eyes open.

Where did you choose to go? Why?

Describe how the trees, plants, and other natural elements were different from what you see in your neighborhood.

Has this walk inspired you to travel even farther to another state park?

College

WALK

Academic campuses are often some of the most pedestrian-friendly outdoor spaces.

They're typically designed with plenty of pathways, crosswalks, and areas to roam without worrying about cars and trucks. There are so many historic colleges and universities across America, and it's fun to explore the architecture. Some are spread out and cover acres of beautiful landscape, which are wonderful to photograph and see through the seasons. Depending on when you visit, you'll likely experience one of two environments: the hustle and bustle of students hurrying to class during the school year or the quiet and calm during the summer months and holidays. And who knows—you might even find shops and restaurants that you didn't know existed tucked around the campus.

1 HOUR

HOW TO DO IT

There are so many picturesque campuses to explore. Here are a few ideas for picking one. You can visit the college in your town or one a few towns away. If you have a family member attending college, ask them for a tour of the grounds. How about your own alma mater? When was the last time you walked your own college campus? Next time you plan to be in the same city as your own school, check it out and see how much it has changed or stayed the same. Venture along the perimeter, the adjacent neighborhoods, or stroll straight through campus.

Where did you walk?

What time of year was it?

Was the campus full of students or a bit quieter?

Did you discover anything you didn't already know was there?

Wide-Open Spaces

WALK

Did you know that your brain goes into a more reflective and calm state when you can see for miles in front of you?

Think of the last time you looked across a wild meadow or a giant grassy lawn. It's almost like staring at a blank canvas. Because these spaces are not crowded with trees or buildings, you can see much farther into the distance than you can when looking at a forest or cityscape.

5+ MINUTES

HOW TO DO IT

This walk is about the body and brain experiencing this space of vastness, which our eyes crave. Even if you only get to try this once in a while, it is worth exploring this type of walk. A short five-minute stroll across a field still helps the entire body relax and unwind. You can do this during the day or in the evening when you can look up at the night sky.

Do you have a wild meadow or field near your house? What's it like?

How did you feel when you purposefully looked far and away?

Did you try this with loved ones or alone?

Family
WALK

Any walk can be a Family Walk, but consider establishing your own traditions to guide how you enjoy your time spent strolling together.

The act of embarking on a journey together, big or small, creates a shared experience, which is ripe for making memories. And like you might've experienced on your Mentor Walk, this walk facilitates open conversation and helps everyone feel more uninhibited. Despite living under the same roof, we spend so much time on our devices that we aren't speaking to each other as often as we could be. A Family Walk helps not only break the ice for delicate conversations, but it also offers a space to simply discuss topics of the day. Often when we walk, we become more empathetic and understanding. We listen more intently.

20-30 MINUTES

HOW TO DO IT

These walks can certainly be impromptu but if you want to plan ahead, after dinner is a good time to get everyone moving. Roam through your neighborhood or drive to a local park where you can experience the beauty of nature together and allow the kids to explore the wildlife of the plants, trees, and rocks. Pick one person to carry a phone for emergency purposes only, and have everyone else go tech-free. Conversations usually flow once you are released from being attached to your devices. Try doing this once a week for starters. If you can do it even more frequently, the family will get into a rhythm of walking and talking together. This is great to start when kids are young.

Describe in detail where you went for a walk.

Who took the lead? Who pointed out the most about your surroundings?
Were you surprised?

Did the conversations feel good?

Bridge

WALK

Whether on your daily commute or while running errands, you likely take bridges to get around.

But when we are zipping by in a car or train, we don't get the chance to appreciate the spectacular views these landmarks provide. A Bridge Walk allows you the time to enjoy this scenery safely. Many bridges are built with some incline, so you might be able to work some more muscles on this one.

15+ MINUTES

HOW TO DO IT

Find the closest bridge to you that has a dedicated walking path, and ask a family member, neighbor, or friend to walk the bridge with you for safety reasons. Check the weather before you go. You'll want to avoid extreme wind, rain, or other inclement weather. As you walk, take time to enjoy the different vantage points the bridge offers. Stop one-third of the way across and take in your surroundings from that perspective. When you get to the halfway point, stop again and see how the perspective has changed, if at all. Try again from three-fourths of the way. You can even try this at different times of the year to see how things change on a larger scale.

Were you surprised at how steep the bridge was to walk?

Did you experience a better workout than you planned for?

What was the weather like?

What buildings or landmarks could you identify from the bridge?

Mood-Boosting

WALK

Having a rough day or week? Feeling a bit overwhelmed?

A long walk in nature may be just what you need to lighten your spirit. How many times have you heard someone say, "I just need to walk this off," or "I just need a good walk to feel better?" Well, there is science behind that statement. When we get outside in nature or just outside of our own four walls, we are moving our bodies and allowing ourselves to breathe in harmony with our walking. Once we begin to truly walk and breathe and get out of our own minds, we begin to be more present. We open our eyes to the beauty around us (like that cute puppy that just walked by or the scent of jasmine from a nearby tree). By going outside and walking, you are giving yourself permission to step into your body and breathe in a new, positive way.

10 MINUTES

HOW TO DO IT

When you begin to feel overwhelmed, it can be hard to motivate yourself to move at all, but this is when we need it the most. When you walk, your body releases its happy hormone, called endorphins. If you're having trouble getting the energy to head outside, start by remembering that your walk is your medicine, a natural mood booster. Then, head out the door with no expectations or goals other than to walk for 10 minutes. If you are feeling a bit better, try going for a few more minutes. The more often you use walking to enhance your mood, the more you will want to do it.

How far did you walk?

Did you see new things?

What was the weather like?

Will you do this again if you begin to feel anxious or worried and just need a good boost?

Heel-Toe
WALK

Connect with your body in a new way.

Walking is second nature to us. When we were babies, we began that forward motion of movement from crawling, to standing and swaying, to those first steps forward. Our bodies are meant to walk. Yet we often end up feeling disconnected from the experience. We wear shoes that encase our feet so we lose the sensation of our feet on the ground below us. A Heel-Toe Walk is a liberating exercise to get you back in touch with your stride. You might feel silly doing it, but moving your body in an unusual way can help you slow down and observe what your body actually feels like, something that often fades into the background as we rush from place to place.

5 MINUTES

HOW TO DO IT

Try this walk in your yard, a park, or anywhere you can take your shoes off. If you can't go barefoot, you'll still feel a connection, but removing your shoes will make tuning into the sensation easier. Take a step with your right leg and land with your right heel hitting the ground first, followed by the rest of your foot. Repeat on the left side and continue for the entirety of your walk. Practice being aware of the feeling of your heel touching the ground and then your toes. If you are barefoot, spread out your toes and wiggle them around so your entire foot is grabbing the earth below it. It feels good, doesn't it?

Do your feet feel free when you are trying this without shoes on?

Did you experience a different sensation walking like this?

Did you find it easy or difficult to focus on your feet? How long did your attention stay on your stride?

Stair
WALK

With a little mindfulness, every stairway can lead to a better mood.

Hiking up and down a flight or two requires more coordination and awareness than your typical walk in the park, so this exercise will help you get your mind focused on the task at hand. Plus, you'll boost your heart rate and engage muscles that don't get as much action on flat ground.

5 MINUTES

HOW TO DO IT

If you don't have stairs in your home, there are plenty of places to log some steps. Think sports stadiums, office buildings, the path leading to a museum, a local park, etc. Look for at least 20 to 30 stairs in total and walk up and down those stairs two or three times. Move your arms back and forth as you go. A Stair Walk can become a part of your interval workouts if you throw in a more challenging move every few steps, like taking two stairs at a time. This will raise your heart rate and get the blood pumping. The more you do this, the better you will get.

Where did you find your steps?

What muscles did you feel working to get you up the stairs?

Was it a great workout for you?

When do you plan to try it again?

Community
WALK

Want to bring the community together and learn from one another?

Set up a group walk. You'll create a no-pressure space for meeting new people and getting to know neighbors better. Traditional community meeting settings might feel daunting for some (like standing up at a town hall), so a relaxed stroll through a park can encourage more casual and productive conversation.

20-30 MINUTES

HOW TO DO IT

To get the message out to a large community, work with your local government offices, town halls, schools, libraries, or even the local small business district. Create and distribute a walk/talk calendar and help people match with others they don't know to just walk for 20 or 30 minutes. Try this on a Saturday and get a large group of people to walk together but in pairs. Establish a route that ends at a local restaurant and enjoy some food afterward. See if you can keep it going once a month, and don't forget to invite new community members!

How many people did you get to sign up?

What did you talk about on the walk? Did you feel more connected to your community?

What was the outcome?

Art

WALK

Once you've tried photographing your walk, consider a new artistic approach: sketching.

Unlike photography, which captures your subject exactly as it is, drawing allows you to interpret what you see through your own lens. Because you can't point and click to get your image, sketching requires you to spend more time focusing on the object in front of you. You may find you get to know the mailbox at the end of your block better than ever before!

↓

30+ MINUTES

HOW TO DO IT

Grab a notepad and sketching pencil or charcoal—whatever you might want to use is totally up to you. Even the back of a napkin works! As you walk, what stands out to you? Do you see a beautiful tree? Maybe it's an interesting fence or garden. Stop and take a few minutes to draw what you see. Keep walking and sketching the things that catch your eye.

What inspired you and/or your family to draw?

Did you see something truly beautiful or new?

What details did you notice about your subject that you might've missed before?

Zoo

WALK

Zoos provide plenty of sprawling walkways and green paths, enough to spend the entire day meandering around.

Just like an amusement park or fair, zoos are filled with sensory experiences that can help pull you back to the present—the roar of a lion, the laughter of children. With all the excitement of visiting the animals, you might not realize how many miles you can clock just from roaming amongst the exhibits.

1+ HOURS

HOW TO DO IT

You can do this alone or with younger family members or even aging adults. Head into this walk with all your senses activated. As you make your way through the zoo, listen for all the different animal noises, the sound of nearby chatter, or the whir of a golf cart. There will also be so many different smells throughout.

What was your favorite animal to see?

What new things did you notice about the zoo?

Describe your experience of seeing the animals. Did you sense any animals taking notice of you?

Reading

WALK

Here's a fun little challenge to try: Grab the book you're currently reading, and try making your way through a few pages while slowly walking.

It may sound impossible, but some people find that the movement helps them process every sentence better than being stationary. You'll engage different parts of your brain simultaneously, which can be a refreshing change of pace. Plus, if you can master this, you'll never have to put down that page-turner!

HOW TO DO IT

To perform this walk safely, find a large space without any obstacles, far from any roads and other people. Your own backyard or a running track could work well. As you attempt this, remember that it's OK if you don't quite get the hang of it. This takes practice and some coordination, so it isn't for everyone. The process of attempting something new is valuable in itself.

How many pages or chapters did you read on your walk?

How long did you walk?

Was it difficult for you to walk while reading? What part of the movement was most challenging?

Sunset WALK

After a long day, watching the sun dip below the horizon may be just what you need to find balance again.

Sunsets can be a reminder of the cyclical nature of life and how no matter how stressful things get, the sun will always come up tomorrow. But more than that, this special hour of the day is a chance to witness the explosion of colors in the sky, an event that can easily bring your awareness back to the present moment and into a state of awe. This walk can truly be refreshing for your body, soul, and spirit.

20 MINUTES

HOW TO DO IT

Identify a place with a great vantage point for watching the sun set and a walking path leading to it, maybe a mountaintop, bridge, hill, or a large clearing. Research the exact time the sun sets in your region, and then plan to get to your destination about 10 minutes before that time. Sometimes the sky begins to change colors 20 to 30 minutes before the sun actually sets, and this can be breathtaking to experience. Observing this gradient of colors is stunning on its own but you can tie many different walks into this, such as the Photography Walk on page 108 or the Art Walk on page 134. Don't worry about how many steps you take. This is about experiencing the beauty around you.

Did you go alone or with someone else?

What did the sunset feel like?

What was the walk like? Were there others around?

Ball

WALK

**Do you want
to practice hand-eye coordination?**

Grab a basketball or any bouncy ball that is the size of your palm or larger, and start dribbling as you walk. Many of the games and activities from childhood are also useful tools for sharpening your coordination skills, yet as we get older we often stop playing. This simple and inexpensive exercise will help reignite your fun-loving side and make you feel more sure on your feet.

5 MINUTES

HOW TO DO IT

Stake out a spot on your driveway or other paved area with room to move. Start walking and begin to bounce the ball with each step. It's not easy! But keep at it. This walk is not about how many steps you take but rather about moving your body and doing something that you may not have done before. Challenge yourself to see how far you can walk and bounce the ball without it straying away from you.

Did you have fun trying this out?

Was it easier or harder than you thought it would be? Why?

Did this walk remind you of games you played as a kid? What memories does it evoke when you think about it?

Nature Terrain

WALK

The world is brimming with various types of landscapes, all of which offer a different sensation as you stride across them.

There are squishy mossy trails, sandy shorelines, crunchy gravel paths, root-covered routes—you get the idea. Each comes with its own sounds and feelings (and perhaps scents) for you to notice and focus on. The variety pays off physically as well. We need to move our bodies in different ways, especially our feet, so we don't lose our mobility. We spend most of our lives on flat surfaces—in our homes, workplaces, and everywhere in between. If you can give your feet something new to walk over, like rocks or tree roots, you'll help strengthen those muscles, plus your legs.

20 MINUTES

HOW TO DO IT

Put on shoes with good traction, such as sneakers or walking shoes, and head out to terrain that is not concrete or paved. If you can find shoes that are as close to grounding as possible but still offer protection, use them. Your feet and toes will try and grab the ground beneath you. As you walk, notice how your whole body moves differently over uneven terrain. Do you use your arms more? Do you feel your abs tighten?

Where did you find the terrain?

How did the path differ from concrete or pavement? Did it feel, sound, look, or even smell different?

What did you see on your walk?

Midday
WALK

Many people love a walk in the morning or evening, but have you tried stepping out in the middle of your day?

There might be no better cure for the midday work slump. After all, you know how effective walking is at igniting creativity and boosting your mood. If you spend your workday sitting, this is also a great excuse to stretch your legs and shake out stiff body parts. Think of this as a brisk walk to get the blood flowing and creative juices pumping.

20 MINUTES

HOW TO DO IT

Consider scheduling your Midday Walk on your work calendar just like you would schedule a meeting. This will help you break away from your desk and get you into the habit of hitting the pavement in the middle of the day. If you want to listen to music, that's fine, but hold off on making or taking any calls—this walk is just about you. Walk briskly, enjoy the fresh air and the movement of your body. Feel free to shake your arms and legs. If it's raining, walk the space or stairs in your home.

What were you working on and how did you feel before your walk?

How did you feel after? When you sat back down, did you feel refreshed?

How can you get in the habit of taking walks during the day like this?

Kindness
WALK

Open your heart and put on your shoes—it's time to drop off notes of kindness.

A Kindness Walk is an opportunity to share a little joy by leaving pieces of paper with positive messages for others to find. It doesn't matter if you know your neighbors, if you live in a cul-de-sac or apartment building, or if you have anything creative to say. This is all about spreading kindness to those around you. The practice of writing cheerful notes will help you focus on the good and give others a little boost as well.

1+ HOURS

HOW TO DO IT

Purchase notecards or use blank paper to create your own. Write something uplifting, like a friendly "hello," your favorite quote, or an inspirational affirmation. Add extra cheer with colored markers. Once you've written all your notes, drop them off in neighbors' mailboxes or front doors.

What kind of card did you create?

Did you wind up seeing any of your neighbors while you were delivering your notes? What was the interaction like?

How long did it take you to hand out the cards? How did you feel after?

Wheelchair

WALK

An opportunity to walk alongside or behind a wheelchair is a special gift.

If you're reading this book, you've likely been blessed with the ability to use your legs to walk. You can share the joy of moving through outdoor spaces with people who use wheelchairs by assisting them in getting outside for some fresh air. Think about how good you feel when you can get outside for a stroll, even if it is just for a few minutes. Everyone deserves that experience. It's a wonderful way to bond conversationally with someone, but even if the individual can't speak, you are still participating in a shared experience. That is a special opportunity and one that can be done regularly.

20 MINUTES

HOW TO DO IT

There are many ways and opportunities to do this. You may have a family member in a wheelchair or know of someone who is in one. Take the time to see if you can walk with them or help them. There are also volunteer programs at local assisted living facilities or homes for the disabled that often would love help. Call and see what kinds of programs they have and get involved.

Did you walk with someone new? Who?

How did this walk make you feel?

Did it give you a new sense of appreciation for your ability to walk?

Waterway

WALK

Oceans, rivers, streams, and waterfalls all have a very powerful effect on us.

There is a scientific reason people feel so good when they are around or walking near bodies of water that continuously move. When water is moving freely, it releases negative ions. We then inhale these invisible molecules. Once they enter our bloodstream, the biochemical response within us increases our serotonin, which helps relieve stress, alleviate depression, and boost our energy. The negative ions are not released along stagnant bodies of waters like ponds or lakes. Next time you need an extra boost of energy or want to feel better, skip the coffee and go to your nearest waterway to walk.

20 MINUTES

HOW TO DO IT

Find a gentle waterway near you with a trail beside it. Enjoy this walk at your own pace. Inhale deeply as you walk and, if you are able to, reach out and touch the water. Notice how it feels on your skin and the sensation of the water as it dries on your hand. Stop at different points along the waterway. Does the air around you change? Can you sense the water on your skin? Depending on where you do this and the time of year, you might notice the temperature drop as you get close to the water, due to the water temperature being cooler than the air around you. Watch how the vegetation changes as you walk. Also listen to the sounds of the waterway and what noises are man-made versus those that are from nature.

Did you touch the water you were walking next to? Describe how it felt.

How did you feel after this walk?

Where did you go?

Forage
WALK

On your next stroll through your neighborhood, keep your eyes open for interesting (or edible!) plants to collect and bring home.

Although we luckily do not need to forage for our food anymore, there is still joy to be had in the process of spotting and identifying local vegetation that is safe to eat or simply beautiful enough to display in a vase. For example, if you find fragrant lavender, pick a little bit and place it on your nightstand to help you sleep at night. Or do some research to discover what native plants might bear fruit in your area. A Forage Walk will help you better understand the resources that grow naturally in your neighborhood.

30 MINUTES

HOW TO DO IT

Research what grows naturally in your town and when it is in season. Maybe there are wild and safe mushrooms that exist locally. Ask local growers what they forage for or talk to a farm-to-table restaurant. You might be surprised how many edible items are growing around you. Be warned, it is illegal to forage in certain areas or parks.

What is grown local to you that is edible?

Did you go out on a Forage Walk and find some great items to add to a dish or to your home?

Were you surprised by what you found out?

Skip

WALK

When was the last time you actually skipped?

If you can't remember, this is the perfect time to try again. Like the Crab Walk on page 68 and the Heel-Toe Walk on page 128, skipping is an opportunity to move your entire body in a way you're likely not used to. Your arms will swing, your knees will rise, and you'll probably laugh.

↓

1 MINUTE

HOW TO DO IT

If you're not comfortable skipping down the sidewalk, clear some space in your home or yard and get to it! This is not about steps or length but more about movement and joy.

Did you smile as you skipped? How did you feel?

Did you try this inside or outside?

Did skipping come back to you naturally or did it take your body some time to remember how to do it?

Creative
WALK

Although we can't control when creativity strikes, we can put our mind and body in prime position for a wave of inspiration.

A walk in nature will do just that. As you immerse yourself in a world outside your desk, you'll find it's easier to relax and become absorbed into the beauty of your surroundings (instead of racking your brain for a new idea for work). Don't stress if nothing comes to you during the course of the walk. This practice helps you declutter your mind, allowing more space for new ideas to arise right then or 20 minutes into the walk.

20 MINUTES

HOW TO DO IT

Skip the headphones and complete this walk completely in tune with your environment, whether that's a city street or a suburban office complex. Walk slowly and feel your feet as they connect with the pavement. Let this walk be very intentional. As you walk, look for cues around you that might spark interest. Watch how the sunlight hits different objects, like the side of a house or undersides of leaves in the trees. Consider how light continually changes every day, morning through night, as the sun moves across the sky. Every day and moment offers a new experience for you to draw inspiration. As ideas arise, note them on paper or record a voice memo on your phone.

What time of day did you go?

Did you see something you weren't expecting?

List five things you saw that were the color blue.

Resilience
WALK

After a setback, whether personal or professional, this walk can help you recover.

When you find yourself doubting your ability to move ahead, try this reflective exercise. A Resilience Walk involves observing the patterns in nature to remind you of your own true tough-cookie nature. Those cues might be as small as an ant carrying a crumb on its back or as large as ivy covering and reclaiming an abandoned building. Nature is resilient and so are you, always. Nature has to go through the seasons of life, as do you. A Resilience Walk should motivate you to keep moving forward, to keep climbing, to keep stumbling, to keep trying. No one's path is perfect, and when you walk and realize all that you have done and how far you have come, you begin to feel better.

15+ MINUTES

HOW TO DO IT

Go anywhere with some nature—a park, tree-lined street, or hiking trail—and look all around you. Walk for at least 15 minutes and feel how good it is to be alive in the moment. Think about all that you have learned so far. Sometimes when we walk, we stumble, but that is where the grace is. That is where the beauty of sprouting back anew and the inspiration to never stop trying, growing, and evolving lives.

Did you learn something about yourself today?

What does resilience mean to you?

Do you ever think about how resilient you truly are? How did you get that way?

Posture

WALK

For this excursion, direct your attention to how you hold yourself.

Often, we fall into less-than-perfect posture thanks to hours spent craning our necks toward a computer screen or smartphone. This is a chance to zone in on your back, shoulders, and neck and discover what position you default to. Once you become more aware of your body when you move, you become more in tune with what feels good when you walk. What are the shoes you usually wear every day when you are at home or at work? How do those shoes make your feet and body feel? If you are not comfortable in your daily shoes, your posture will be off.

↓

15+ MINUTES

HOW TO DO IT

You will need to do this walk with shoes and barefoot, so try this one wherever you are comfortable kicking off your shoes. Start first by wearing your shoes and walking as you normally would. Does your body feel aligned? Breathe deeply and mindfully as you go. Do your shoes allow you to walk tall with your back straight? Try this with various pairs of shoes (your most comfortable and your least comfortable should be good enough) and then once barefoot. Take note of how your foot hits the ground and how this impacts your posture. Finally, try walking with good posture— stand tall and keep your back straight.

How did you feel when you were cognizant of walking with your back straight?

What posture does your body fall into when you're not actively trying to stand tall? Does your posture change as you walk?

How comfortable are you in your shoes? How do they impact your posture?

Problem-Solving
WALK

Are you faced with a challenge at work or on a team that you are a part of?

Are you trying to figure out a problem in the office? Many of these meetings are held indoors at a large table or in a large room. Why don't you suggest that for the next meeting you all go somewhere for a walk? Maybe you propose going for a group walk for 15 minutes before you head indoors for your meeting. Maybe the entire meeting is walking. Is there a topic that has been tough to resolve or needs a better path to a positive outcome?

15 MINUTES

HOW TO DO IT

Find a convenient place to walk and set the stage for a different way to have the meeting. If you can only walk the perimeter of the office space, that's fine. Before you begin, let everyone know the walk is intended to be a space for thinking freely and openly about the problem. Suggest the group gather for a walk, pair up, and walk side by side behind one another. Start walking and talking about ideas and suggestions. Bring a notepad to jot down possible outcomes as you go.

Was the group engaged in the walk?

Were the discussions interesting and helpful?

Where did you wind up going for this walk?

Confidence
WALK

Build more than muscles out there!

The Posture Walk on page 162 taught you to be aware of your posture while walking. Now, take that one step forward and add some confidence. It may sound cheesy, but you spend so much time putting one foot in front of the other each day—why not use it to boost your self-esteem? Sometimes when we are in a rush we don't even realize the body language we are using. Maybe your head is down or your arms are crossed. Take some time to position your body in a way that you think reads as "confident," and see how you feel.

20 MINUTES

HOW TO DO IT

Test out some different postures that make you feel proud. Perhaps your back is straight, your stride is long and comfortable, your chin is up. Spend this time just enjoying how you move, and don't worry too much about time or distance. Keep it up!

Did you feel different than when you walk normally?

How did you hold your body during this walk?

What made you feel confident today?

Memory
WALK

Try taking a stroll down memory lane.

We all have physical places that hold special meaning to us. It might be the park where your partner proposed, the street where you lived in your first apartment, or the trail that you used to hike with a loved one. Revisiting these spaces will likely bring up memories of the past, which you can use to observe the contrast of the present. You'll notice the things that have changed and all the good things that will always stay the same.

30+ MINUTES

HOW TO DO IT

Think about pivotal moments in your life. Where did they occur? Can you go take a walk near those places? Enter this walk mindful of all the little details around you—how the sidewalk looks (is it more weathered than when you last saw it?), the way nearby buildings have changed, and the sounds that surround you. These seemingly small elements define a sense of place and will help you appreciate all the happy memories you have.

Describe in as much detail as possible this place as it was the last time you saw it.

What has changed about it? What has stayed the same?

What sounds did you hear on this walk?

Picnic
WALK

Turn your next walk into an alfresco meal with friends.

It's simple enough to drive to your picnic destination, but the act of carrying your meal and trekking out to your spot makes every bite that much sweeter. You'll get extra time soaking in the fresh air plus a chance to get into a more mindful headspace as your breath and steps fall into line.

HOW TO DO IT

Find a picnicking location that you can easily walk to, maybe in a park, on a hillside, or a beach. As you make your way to the picnic, take in all of your surroundings. The air on your skin, the sights, the sounds of the people in the space, the laughter, the conversations. Maintain that same awareness once you dig into your food. Observe the aroma, the look, the feeling, sounds, and taste of each bite.

Who did you picnic with?

How was eating outdoors different from where you typically eat?

Wildlife
WALK

Broaden your search for the creatures we share our planet with.

Increase your chance of a wildlife encounter with this fun walk, in which you'll scope out any and all wildlife. You might be surprised—and humbled—by the fact that there is life, big and small, all around you. Although nature preserves might hold the most potential for catching a glimpse of critters, keep your eyes open for signs of life on all your walks. It'll help anchor you in your immediate surroundings.

30+ MINUTES

HOW TO DO IT

Head to your favorite park and start looking. Look up into the trees, the trunks, the branches, the roots. Minimize distractions and leave your phone in your pocket. Use more than just your eyes to detect creatures. Listen for the rustle of leaves or snapping of twigs. If you choose to do this type of walk in a nature preserve or state park, read the guidelines and do some research to learn what animals are commonly spotted in the area. Keep a ledger or diary of what you see or spot and what time of year it is. Repeat this throughout the year to observe how wildlife patterns change with the season.

What did you see? Did you see or hear it first?

What did you feel when you saw it?

Did you go alone or with family?

Treasure Map

WALK

The thrill of a scavenger hunt is a surefire way to get everyone moving.

Once you and your family and friends get into the hunt, you may clock thousands of steps without realizing it. In addition to being a playful form of exercise, the Treasure Map Walk is, in many ways, a mindfulness walk. Everyone will need to pay attention to spot treasures and note the paths they've already traveled so as not to retrace their steps.

45 MINUTES

HOW TO DO IT

This walk can be elaborate or quite simple. Pick a place to host the treasure hunt, such as your yard or around your neighborhood, then draw a map of the area (or print one using Google Maps). Round up a collection of "treasures" to hide (think small items, like toy cars or painted rocks) and mark where they are hidden with an "X" on your map. Give everyone a copy of the map and set out to search for the prizes together.

Was everyone involved having fun?

How long was everyone outside looking for the treasures?

Do you want to do this again?

Learn a Language

WALK

Have you always wanted to learn a new language but think you don't have the time to do so?

Maybe you just want to pick up a few words but keep putting it off for another day? Instead of turning on music or a podcast, tune into a new language as you walk. There are plenty of apps that offer audio-only language classes. You'll save time by bundling your learning with your exercise. Plus, we often can think more clearly as we walk, step, breathe, and speak out loud.

30+ MINUTES

HOW TO DO IT

Download a language app on your smartphone and start walking your favorite route. Begin reciting the words and phrases out loud as you step forward. Try doing this type of learning walk versus sitting down at home, and see how much more you retain on your walk. Try this for 15 minutes at a time every day if you are aiming to learn a language for an upcoming event.

Did you recall more than you expected on this walk?

How far did you walk?

Were you comfortable on your walk?

Color
WALK

See if you can spy the rainbow on your everyday route!

We have the gift of being able to see an incredible range of colors throughout our everyday life. From the moment you wake up you're exposed to a spectrum of hues. Have you ever noticed how many different shades of green there are in the natural world? Or the way colors become more vibrant or muted depending on the time of day? Paying attention to these nuances can help direct your attention to the here and now. Who knows? You might even find a new favorite color!

10+ MINUTES

HOW TO DO IT

This walk is especially fun to do with a partner, but you are welcome to do it solo as well. Head outside and take in the gradient of color around you. Notice how the sun and shadows can make a single object appear to include dozens of different shades of the same color. Using the colors of the rainbow (red, orange, yellow, green, blue, indigo, and violet) as your guide, begin to identify objects of each color. For example, for red you might spot the taillight of a car or berries on a bush. Work your way through these seven colors then repeat the process throughout your walk as your scenery changes.

What color did you see the most during your walk? List what you saw.

What color was hardest to find? Where did you end up finding it?

Using all your senses, describe one green object you saw.

Full-Body Awareness

WALK

During a typical day, you likely don't have to think much about the space between your body and everything else.

Unless you live in a tiny space, you probably can walk freely without fear of knocking into anything. Maybe you take advantage of this and spend your time afoot buried in your smartphone without much awareness of how far you are from your surroundings. This walk will help snap you back into spatial awareness and overall mindfulness. Once you begin walking like this, you will become much more in tune with your surroundings, the sights, and smells—plus the feeling your body receives from those cues around you.

15 MINUTES

HOW TO DO IT

You can do this anywhere. The key is being aware of your body as you walk, so unplug and give your body your full attention. Notice how close you are to other people as they walk past you. How far is that branch above your head? What about that bird that just flew by? Focus on one thing at a time.

Did you notice others around you not aware of their surroundings?

List five things you walked by that were close enough to touch.

What did you notice about the space you occupy as you walk? Do you zigzag on your path or stick to one side?

Leaf

WALK

A fall walk through the leaves is a treat for the senses.

You will hear the rustle of the leaves, feel them crunching as they crack apart, and smell the scent of dried plants and crisp autumn air.

15 MINUTES

HOW TO DO IT

On the next autumn day, when you see leaf piles around your neighborhood, head out for a good romp in them! Maybe the leaves have piled up along a path that you regularly walk; walk through those leaves versus walking on the path itself. Let your body enjoy the sensations of this walk and how the path differs from other times of year. Perhaps the soil is drier or there is an earthy scent in the air. Don't forget to notice the changing colors of the leaves beneath your feet and all around you.

What month did you walk in?

Where were the leaves most vibrant? What colors did you see?

What did you smell when you walked in the leaves?

How crunchy and dry are the leaves? How loud is the sound when you walk on them?

Hill

WALK

Walking at an incline is sure to activate not only your muscles in a new way, but also your mind.

You'll be forced to think about your movement pattern a little differently than you would on flat ground. You'll also engage different muscles in your legs and feet to support and move you. Best of all, your efforts will lead you to what is sure to be an amazing view.

20 MINUTES

HOW TO DO IT

Walk or drive to the nearest hill in your neighborhood. Slowly make your way up the hill and observe how your body feels and what muscles seem to be working the hardest. Notice the ground beneath you. Is it rugged terrain or a grassy hill? Can you smell the ground and air around you? Turn around and walk downhill. Are you carrying yourself differently than on your way uphill? Walk up and down the hill a few times. This is more about experiencing the movement you are putting your body through versus challenging yourself to hit an intense speed. If you get to the point where you want to walk faster, then definitely do so.

Where did the hill lead? Describe the view.

Did you notice you needed to consciously balance when walking back down the hill?

What was your favorite part of this walk?

Building

WALK

Just as the natural landscape around us changes with the months and years, so does the man-made landscape.

In a given year in your neighborhood, a new parking garage might be built, a neighbor might install a fresh mailbox, or a building might be knocked down. Paying attention to the details of the buildings around you can foster a more mindful headspace plus keep you up to date on community happenings.

30 MINUTES

HOW TO DO IT

Walk to an area of your neighborhood with a lot of buildings. Observe the architecture and the details that make each structure unique. If you live in a city, you might be watching a new building going up. Notice how it changes the landscape of the block. If you live in a community where houses line the blocks, you might see that someone has painted their front door or added a fence. Take a mental note of these details, and repeat this walk in a few months.

How is the man-made landscape around you changing?

Did you notice any similarities in the buildings around you?

What type of building did you see the most of?

Yard

WALK

This might sound simple, but we don't often take time to walk on our own property and get to know the nuances that make it home.

Big or small, a yard provides outdoor space to log some steps and get fresh air. Typically, we focus solely on the areas that require maintenance, like the grass or the weeds. But there is another level to explore that will help you foster your attention to detail and a greater appreciation for your home and local ecology. The more you get into the practice of walking your yard, the more you will want to care for it to watch it bloom into its full potential.

15 MINUTES

HOW TO DO IT

Start by walking the perimeter of your yard. Notice what is sprouting up, weeds and all. What kind of life exists there (bugs, bees, birds)? Tune into the scents you come across and the sounds that arise. Repeat this process with the rest of your outdoor space.

Did you see a lot more than you thought you would in your yard?

Did this walk prompt you to want to do something with the space you have?

What time of year is it? How does your yard look at other times of the year?

Garage Sale

WALK

In some ways, a cruise through your neighborhood yard sales is the ultimate game of I Spy.

Tables are cluttered with items big and small, and it takes great attention to detail to unearth a real treasure. Build off the mindfulness you've been cultivating and see if you can walk in full awareness through the sales this Saturday. You'll up your step tally, connect with neighbors, and maybe even find a diamond in the rough!

1 HOUR

HOW TO DO IT

Check community websites and social media groups to find out when the next community yard sale is. Head out alone or in a group, and if you have to drive to a location, park a decent distance away from the address so you can walk a little before you arrive. Think about what you are seeing all around you, from the houses to the scents to the time of year. Is it a fall day with pumpkins decorating many doorsteps? Be sure to check back in with yourself between each stop to make sure you are walking in mindfulness.

Did you see friends and neighbors?

Did you wind up purchasing anything?

What item did you see the most of? What was the most interesting object you saw for sale?

Friend

WALK

**Haven't seen a friend
in a long time?**

Instead of heading out for a happy hour, invite them over for a
walking hour. You already know that walks help facilitate a calm
and comfortable atmosphere for conversation, so you'll likely
connect with your pal more deeply than you might in a noisy bar.
You can share life updates and scope out any changes in your
neighborhood as well. And with a great walking partner, you may
realize you can walk even farther than on your own. Your body,
brain, and heart will thank you for it.

HOW TO DO IT

A walk with friends is a great social activity and can be done all year long and anywhere, no matter where you live. Consider starting a walking group and plan to meet up for strolls regularly throughout the year. If a rainy day comes along, don't let that deter you. You may even want to get together and work through the walks in this book!

Did you smile and laugh on your walk with a friend(s)?

Did you stay local or wind up going somewhere else?

How many people walked together?

Old Train Tracks

WALK

In many towns, you'll find stretches of land covered by unused, decades-old train tracks.

These areas are often surrounded by vegetation—some of it growing directly over the tracks, making them unexpected and off-the-beaten-path nature trails. These areas are ripe for exploration and are brimming with local history.

20 MINUTES

HOW TO DO IT

Research where to find unused train tracks near you, and be sure to confirm that they are truly no longer operating. Always keep noise distractions, like music or podcasts, off on these walks. You may want to also spend some time learning about the history of the tracks beforehand to help add context to your stroll. On your walk, observe what's growing around the tracks. How was the natural landscape changed to accommodate the tracks and how is it evolving now that trains no longer pass through? Put on your exploration hat and good walking shoes and see what unfolds around you.

Why are those tracks no longer in service?

When were they used last? When were they put there?

What memories of trains do you have?

Hotel

WALK

**It might surprise you,
but the area surrounding a hotel can often
be a beautiful place to walk.**

Many hotels around the country are maximizing their outdoor spaces
to create a connection to the local ecosystem. Take advantage of these
interesting outdoor areas and get your steps in!

15 MINUTES

HOW TO DO IT

Research some hotels near you to see if they have green space for walking. If you aren't sure
whether or not the space is open to the public, ask the front desk. Explore the surroundings.
Perhaps consider how it might feel to experience them as a visitor from another town, like the
guests in the hotel. You might discover what makes your home so special.

Did you find a hotel that you didn't know was close by?

Was it the first time you walked the property that you chose?

Did you go with a friend or by yourself?

Single-Leg Balance

WALK

Gently shake up your routine with this unusual exercise.

The Single-Leg Balance Walk helps boost strength and balance, while engaging your mind in something new.

5 MINUTES

HOW TO DO IT

Give yourself as much room as possible to walk a straight line. Stand straight and lift your right knee up to waist height, while keeping your left leg securely planted on the ground. Hold for 10 seconds, then step forward with your right leg. Lift your left knee straight up with your right foot securely planted on the ground, hold for 10 seconds, then use your left leg to step forward. Continue this motion, taking small steps and focusing on your balance each time you raise your leg. If you want to make things a bit tougher, raise and hold your arms above your head each time you raise a leg. You can also add a small ankle weight to build muscle.

How was your balance?

Will you continue to try to build on this?

Did you do this outside or inside?

Sports Team
WALK

Team sports are usually all about the physical activity that is being practiced, whether that's bowling or baseball.

But the mental energy you bring to the game is just as important as your technical skills. A pregame walk as a team can help clear everyone's mind and bring a sense of quiet and calm before the hustle and bustle begins. Plus, a noncompetitive stroll allows players room to bond and chat about whatever they like. This walk works well for both adult sports teams and children's leagues.

10+ MINUTES

HOW TO DO IT

Try and incorporate a 10-minute walk with teammates at the beginning of practice. Some members of the team might want to walk and talk, and that's OK. It is the act of gently moving your body to warm up and clear your head that is important. Ask people not to listen to music or use their devices.

How did the team respond to trying this out?

Will you continue to do this with sports you are involved in?

Did people walk alone or form groups to talk?

Yoga

WALK

Get double the relaxation with this soothing stroll, which involves incorporating yoga stretches and poses throughout.

Stopping in the middle of your walk to get into a specific position can help jog your mind back to the present. Use it as a tool to rebalance (literally) while on long walks or when your mind is racing.

15+ MINUTES

HOW TO DO IT

Find a roomy path or trail where you will be able to stop and stretch without being in the way of other walkers. Begin walking at your normal pace. After 2 to 3 minutes, stop and go into one of your favorite yoga poses. Hold for 1 minute. Allow your body to really stretch and your mind to calm down. Begin walking again, stopping to hold a different pose after 2 to 3 minutes. Repeat for as long as you like.

Where did you wind up doing this walk? Did you feel comfortable? Were there a lot of people around?

What did your body feel like when you completed this?

Did you feel more tuned into your surroundings after completing each pose?

History

WALK

There is so much history beneath your feet.

Regardless of how old the buildings and infrastructure are, every town has something to teach us. Tap into it by planning a History Walk. You'll spend an afternoon in the fresh air and leave perhaps with a fresh perspective.

1 HOUR

HOW TO DO IT

Research historic areas or blocks in your town or one nearby. Some cities have small free museums that will introduce you to local history and provide maps to help you find the spots of interest. Pick one with a handful of historic sites in close proximity to each other, and walk from one end to the other. As you walk, stop and observe what makes each location historic. Make a day of it, and support locally owned shops and restaurants.

What historic sites did you see?

What did you learn?

Describe what one of the sites looked like in detail.

Wildflower WALK

Unlike foraging, which can sometimes limit you to a certain month and location to find edible plants and herbs, Wildflower Walks can be done spontaneously and all over.

These pretty blossoms pop up all over—in fields, on the side of the highway, in the cracks of the sidewalk. Perhaps you even consider some of these flowers weeds, but setting out with the intention to find them might make you appreciate their unconventional beauty a little more.

↓

15 MINUTES

HOW TO DO IT

Head to a meadow or field, and roam around. What flowers are growing there? Are they in clusters or formations? Observe how nature grows without direct human intervention. Breathe in the aromas of the flowers and plant life around you. Soak up the beauty of the place and day. Pick your favorite blooms and bring home a little bouquet. Repeat this walk yearly, and you will begin to know when exactly your favorite wildflowers bloom.

What flowers were you able to pick?

Did you choose to tie a ribbon to the nosegay to gift it to someone else or make an arrangement for yourself?

Will you go again before the end of the season to get more blossoms and blooms?

Bike

WALK

For many, biking
is just as calming and centering as a walk,
so why not pair the two together?

A Bike Walk involves biking to your favorite walking route instead of using other modes of transportation. The switch not only buys you more time out in the fresh air, but it can also bring you into a greater state of awareness. Think about getting off a bike after a long ride. You likely feel hyperaware of the muscles you were working. Transitioning into a walk will help you tap further into that awareness.

1 HOUR

HOW TO DO IT

Do a little prep work to find the most bike-friendly route to your walking path. (Check to see if there are places to easily lock up your bike.) These two activities will require you to move your body in very different ways, from the seated pedaling position of a bike to standing tall while walking. Take a moment to notice what muscles and body parts you are engaging in each.

Where did you choose to bike?

Are you considering biking to other walking spots?

Did you go alone or with others?

Client

WALK

Next time you're stressing about a big pitch or meeting, consider swapping the conference room for a loop around the nearest park.

We are often more apt to speak freely when walking outdoors side by side versus sitting in a poorly and artificially lit office staring head-on at attendees. You might find it's easier to explore new conversations in a more natural and organic way. Just as your steps might fall in sync with your client's, so might your ideas. Sometimes just a change of scenery and pace is all you need for more creative thinking to follow.

30 MINUTES

HOW TO DO IT

If a park is not accessible for a place to meet, suggest the perimeter of the office or maybe a nearby tree-lined street. Maybe you or your client has a garden on property and you can suggest taking your meeting there. Wherever you walk, leave your bags in the car, but do come with a pen and a small notepad to jot down ideas.

How well was this idea received?

Did you find that the conversation flowed more freely?

Did you sense that your client was very tuned into what was being discussed?

Sideways WALK

Yes, walking forward is the most efficient way to get around on two legs, but walking sideways might be the most fun.

This exercise requires you to use your legs in a way you typically don't. Although easy, it still requires brain power and attention. And you'll help improve your motor function, balance, and muscle strength.

10 MINUTES

HOW TO DO IT

Give yourself some space for this walk. Take a small step to the right with your right leg, then bring your left leg to meet it. Step out again with your right, and continue repeating this pattern. After a few minutes, switch to leading with your left side. If you find that awkward, you can crouch down an inch or so as you step.

When was the last time you moved side to side?

How did your body feel when you did this on each side?

Did you do this in your yard or where did you choose to go?

Seasonal
WALK

Approach your next walk with the sole intention of observing everything about the current season.

Observe what makes this time of year unique from the moment you open your front door. There are so many little, beautiful details that define winter, spring, summer, and fall, but we rarely take time to notice all of them. Heading outside with this mindset will help you cultivate gratitude and also accept—and even find beauty—in seasonal changes, from heat and humidity to blustery cold. If you live in a region that experiences all four seasons, get to know the peak times of blooms in spring, the greenest of green in summer, the height of fall colors, and the most snowy days of winter.

10+ MINUTES

HOW TO DO IT

Stay mindful of seasonal factors with each step. How does the air feel on your face as you open your front door? What does your body feel like after 10 minutes of walking? Take advantage of what each season brings. Dance in the early spring rain. Make snow angels in the middle of a storm. Walk for miles in the falling leaves. Keep a journal for the seasons, and take pictures to remember the moments of beauty that are given to us. Try this with the entire family so you witness the changes together, and celebrate them as a family.

Do you have a favorite season?

What season did you do this walk? What was the weather like?

Did you do this in your neighborhood or somewhere else?

Birthday
WALK

Happy birthday! Want to kick off your birthday in a truly special way?

Put on your favorite walking shoes and go for a stroll to celebrate you and your special day. Taking the time to log some steps will help you appreciate the gift of movement and your body's ability to move the way it does, no matter your age! What a fun way to enjoy the gift of you and the very special gift of turning another year older. Celebrate that wonderful body you have been given, and get moving outside.

15 MINUTES

HOW TO DO IT

This one is totally freestyle, but you might want to consider creating some sort of tradition you can reflect on every year. For example, you can trek the same waterfall trail annually and observe the changes in the greenery. Or, gather family and friends for a group walk after cake and presents. Whatever you decide, focus on your breath. Inhale deeply and exhale just as deeply as you walk. Direct your thoughts toward love, acceptance, and gratitude for yourself, the very gift of your essence. Enjoy your special day!

Would you do a birthday walk every year?

Would you do this with other loved ones to celebrate their birthdays?

What time of year is your birthday? What was the weather like on your celebratory walk?

Leaf-Peeping
WALK

The breathtaking colors and shapes of autumn leaves are too magnificent to limit to one walk, so consider this a chance to appreciate fall foliage just a little more.

For this exercise, you'll zone in on what you see: the shades of orange, the delicate dance of a leaf in freefall, and the overlap of branches from different trees.

20 MINUTES

HOW TO DO IT

As summer ends, dedicate some time to researching when leaves will hit their peak colors in your region. Pick a walking path with lots of trees and make a plan to visit it once a week, or even daily as the leaves begin to change. Watch how the trees evolve with each passing visit. Incorporate what you learned from the Awe Walk on page 102. Eventually you might be able to identify the trees by the color their leaves turn each autumn.

What colors did you find in your walk?

Were the trees all different colors or were many leaves already on the ground?

What did the air smell like on your walk?

Squat-Step-Squat

WALK

Work up a little sweat with this balance-boosting move.

It combines cardio and muscle-building elements to get your heart pumping and your mind in focus mode.

15 MINUTES

HOW TO DO IT

Stand straight up, take a small step forward with your right leg, and bend down into a semi-kneeling position so your left knee is hovering about an inch above the ground. Bring your left leg to meet your right. Maintaining your squat, walk forward with your left leg, and continue alternating, keeping your arms at your side. For an added challenge, raise your arms above your head. You might find yourself out of breath quickly, and that's OK. Once you get the hang of it, try carrying small weights as you move forward. If you have knee or hip issues, speak to your doctor before attempting this walk.

How did this exercise feel?

Were you tired quickly?

Did you try this outside or inside?

Backwards
WALK

If you can moonwalk, all the better!

Reversing a motion you've done every day since you were a child is sure to get you tuned into each and every step. After all, you can't space out when you run the risk of stumbling. This walk is the ultimate balance test, but more than that, it is a test of your awareness. Make this a part of your regular routine, and you will find yourself much more observant of everything around you.

5 MINUTES

HOW TO DO IT

Make sure you have plenty of room, and consider having someone watch you to avoid collisions. Begin to step slowly backwards. Can you comfortably continue this process uninterrupted? Notice you are now stepping toe, heel, toe, heel—the reverse of your forward stride. This new motion helps your body engage different muscles in your feet and legs. Pay attention to where you experience those sensations.

Did it feel strange at first?

Did you feel off-balance?

Did you try this outside?

Long-Distance WALK

One of the best walks for your body and brain is a Long-Distance Walk.

The longer we walk, the more cardio we get, which benefits the heart and muscles. Your brain continues to benefit from the extended continuous bloodflow and time experiencing nature and fresh air.

1+ HOURS

HOW TO DO IT

This could be done in the city, countryside, beach, mountains— wherever there are miles of uninterrupted paths. Wherever you go, do some prep work first. Check the weather for the day and gear up accordingly. Pack some water or make a plan to stop for some along the way. Finally, warm up with light stretching. The consistent forward motion can leave muscles feeling tight, so limber up as needed. As you walk, notice how your path changes during the course of your journey. Are there a lot of people around? Trees? Birds?

Where did you do this walk?

How long were you gone?

How did you feel afterwards?

Destination
WALK

Truthfully, it is more about the journey than the destination.

But sometimes setting out with a specific end point in mind can renew your gratitude for your other modes of transportation. For this walk, you will leave the car keys at home and hoof it instead.

10+ MINUTES

HOW TO DO IT

What is the next place you have to go within 1 mile of your home? Walk there. It might be the grocery store or a friend's house. If it is only possible to walk one way, then take public transportation home or have someone pick you up.

Where did you opt to go when you walked instead of drove?

How many steps did you take during the walk there and back?

Did you notice anything new that you may have overlooked when you previously took this route?

Senior

WALK

After 98 different walks, you've learned a lot about the power of putting one foot in front of the other.

But perhaps the most powerful thing you can do on a walk is share it with someone else. For this exercise, invite someone older than you to join in. You'll surely feel a little more uplifted by the end and will have given the gift of a good conversation and company.

15 MINUTES

HOW TO DO IT

Local hospitals and senior care centers are often looking for volunteers to help residents get some fresh air and move their bodies. If you have family members who have a hard time getting outside for a stroll, consider taking the time to walk with them. The important thing is to go at your companion's pace and be in the moment. And don't forget to invite the little ones to experience the gift of walking with someone who needs an arm to lean on.

Did you have to go through a course to begin doing this?

Do you have a loved one who needs support to go outside for a walk?

Do you already do this regularly and how does it make you feel?

Charity
WALK

Once you are hooked on walking, you might consistently find yourself looking for opportunities to get in more steps.

Consider participating in or organizing a walkathon for charity. These walks often center around a cause and require attendees to pay a small entry fee, which goes to the charity. You'll get to share your love of walking with something larger than yourself and even affect some positive change in the world.

30+ MINUTES

HOW TO DO IT

Check your local community website and social media groups to find upcoming charity walks near you. If you'd like to create your own, go for it! Walkathons can be big or small, long or short. The key is to find a cause close to your heart and spread the word.

What causes do you care about and why?

List three potential nearby walkathon routes where you could host a walking event for all abilities and ages.

New Horizons
WALK

By now, you have likely logged dozens of miles in your own town and are acutely aware of the sights, sounds, smells, tastes, and feelings of all that is immediately around you.

Great job! Now, it's time to expand your horizons and take the skills you've learned to new sidewalks, trails, and shorelines. You'll find you're better able to absorb the experience of travel and pick up on the beauty that comes from every step, everywhere.

20 MINUTES

HOW TO DO IT

Research your dream walking destination. It could be the Grand Canyon, Yellowstone National Park, Central Park, or maybe the largest mall in America! Determine the time of year with the most ideal weather conditions, and book your trip. This is a great time to have a journal to capture what you see, feel, and experience along the way. Who knows—this might become an annual tradition. No matter what, enjoy the steps along the way.

How did your sensory experience of this walk differ from others? Did you hear or feel something new?

What was the air like? The temperature?

Describe your next dream walking destination.

PART THREE:
Walking
Wellness
Tracker

How to Use The Tracker

Part of the joy of committing to a walking practice is witnessing change. Hopefully the 101 walks helped you observe all the little changes that occur around you throughout the year, from the color of the leaves to the scent in the air. You will likely also have noticed change in yourself. You might have gained more stamina or a more positive attitude. Whatever evolution you've undergone, it's worth writing down. The Walking Wellness Tracker pages in this section are designed to help you document the important details of your walking journey so that you can clearly see your progression and get even more out of every step you take. Below you will find an overview of what each tracker element is and why it's important.

DATE, LOCATION, TIME OF DAY, AND WEATHER

Recording when your walk took place will allow you to see how far you've come over the course of a month, season, or year. It will help you create a benchmark for all other elements you're tracking. Noting the environmental factors, like your location, time of day, and weather, will help you understand how these elements impact your enjoyment of the walk. Perhaps you'll find you get more out of morning walks or that you wake up more refreshed after an evening stroll the day before. Or maybe you find you get your best ideas when you head out right after a rain shower! Whatever the case, these items will help you get a better understanding of what works for you.

DURATION AND DISTANCE

Here is where you might find your walking sweet spot. Track the distance you've traveled (either in miles or steps) and the time you spent on your walk. You might be surprised by how long you actually spent walking. Maybe you tried a walk with a suggested duration of 15 minutes, but you wound up going for 45 minutes. That's a sign of a good time! Also: Don't get discouraged if your pace is slow. For the majority of walks in this book (and life!) what matters most is how present you are, not how fast you go.

WATER

Staying hydrated is so important to ensuring your walks are enjoyable. It's easier to stay mindful and in the moment when you're not thinking about how thirsty you are! Keep track of how much water you drink before, during (if any), and after. If you are going for a short 10- or 20-minute stroll, you might not need to bring water with you. Keeping a log of these things can help you understand how hydration impacts how good you feel on a walk and throughout the rest of your day. Water plays a big role in how you feel all day long.

MOOD

It's remarkable how much a walk can change your attitude. Writing down how you were feeling before and after your walk will help you understand which walks were the biggest mood-boosters. Were you stressed and the walk made you feel better or more connected to

yourself? Did it put you in a better headspace? Maybe you were struggling to get outside at all. Write it all down. This is your space. The more you write, the more you might discover when you look back. You'll discover which walks you want to do over and over again.

ENERGY

From little aches and pains to a bad night's sleep, many things influence the energy you bring to your walks. Documenting your physical state before and after your walks will hopefully show you the energizing power of exercise and inspire you to grab your walking shoes next time you're feeling that midday nap attack. Use this space to note how awake you feel and any body parts that might be causing you trouble before or after your walk.

NOTES

Use these lines to note anything you found special about your walk. If you performed one of the 101 walks, you can record which walk you did and what you liked about it. Write about your sensory experience. Did a particular scent stand out? Were the clouds extra puffy? You can also track these details by sketching or photographing what you saw. When you photograph your walks, you can look back and be reminded of the wonderful time you had. Maybe it will inspire you to repeat that walk or share it with a friend!

Walking Wellness Tracker

DATE	LOCATION	TIME OF DAY

WEATHER

DURATION		
Start Time:	End Time:	Steps:

DISTANCE

WATER		
Before Walk:	During Walk:	After Walk:

MOOD	
Before Walk:	After Walk:

ENERGY	
Before Walk:	After Walk:

NOTES

Walking Wellness Tracker

DATE	LOCATION	TIME OF DAY

WEATHER

DURATION

Start Time:	End Time:	Steps:

DISTANCE

WATER

Before Walk:	During Walk:	After Walk:

MOOD

Before Walk:	After Walk:

ENERGY

Before Walk:	After Walk:

NOTES

Walking Wellness Tracker

DATE	LOCATION	TIME OF DAY

WEATHER

DURATION

Start Time:	End Time:	Steps:

DISTANCE

WATER

Before Walk:	During Walk:	After Walk:

MOOD

Before Walk:	After Walk:

ENERGY

Before Walk:	After Walk:

NOTES

Walking Wellness Tracker

DATE	LOCATION	TIME OF DAY

WEATHER

DURATION

Start Time: End Time: Steps:

DISTANCE

WATER

Before Walk: During Walk: After Walk:

MOOD

Before Walk: After Walk:

ENERGY

Before Walk: After Walk:

NOTES

Walking Wellness Tracker

DATE	LOCATION	TIME OF DAY

WEATHER

DURATION		
Start Time:	End Time:	Steps:

DISTANCE

WATER		
Before Walk:	During Walk:	After Walk:

MOOD	
Before Walk:	After Walk:

ENERGY	
Before Walk:	After Walk:

NOTES

Walking Wellness Tracker

DATE	LOCATION	TIME OF DAY

WEATHER		

DURATION		
Start Time:	End Time:	Steps:

DISTANCE		

WATER		
Before Walk:	During Walk:	After Walk:

MOOD	
Before Walk:	After Walk:

ENERGY	
Before Walk:	After Walk:

NOTES

Walking Wellness Tracker

DATE	LOCATION	TIME OF DAY

WEATHER		

DURATION		
Start Time:	End Time:	Steps:

DISTANCE		

WATER		
Before Walk:	During Walk:	After Walk:

MOOD	
Before Walk:	After Walk:

ENERGY	
Before Walk:	After Walk:

NOTES

Walking Wellness Tracker

DATE	LOCATION	TIME OF DAY

WEATHER

DURATION

Start Time:	End Time:	Steps:

DISTANCE

WATER

Before Walk:	During Walk:	After Walk:

MOOD

Before Walk:	After Walk:

ENERGY

Before Walk:	After Walk:

NOTES

Walking Wellness Tracker

DATE	LOCATION	TIME OF DAY

WEATHER		

DURATION		
Start Time:	End Time:	Steps:

DISTANCE		

WATER		
Before Walk:	During Walk:	After Walk:

MOOD	
Before Walk:	After Walk:

ENERGY	
Before Walk:	After Walk:

NOTES

Walking Wellness Tracker

DATE	LOCATION	TIME OF DAY

WEATHER

DURATION

Start Time:	End Time:	Steps:

DISTANCE

WATER

Before Walk:	During Walk:	After Walk:

MOOD

Before Walk:	After Walk:

ENERGY

Before Walk:	After Walk:

NOTES

Walking Wellness Tracker

DATE	LOCATION	TIME OF DAY

WEATHER		

DURATION		
Start Time:	End Time:	Steps:

DISTANCE		

WATER		
Before Walk:	During Walk:	After Walk:

MOOD	
Before Walk:	After Walk:

ENERGY	
Before Walk:	After Walk:

NOTES

Walking Wellness Tracker

DATE	LOCATION	TIME OF DAY

WEATHER

DURATION

Start Time:	End Time:	Steps:

DISTANCE

WATER

Before Walk:	During Walk:	After Walk:

MOOD

Before Walk:	After Walk:

ENERGY

Before Walk:	After Walk:

NOTES

Walking Wellness Tracker

DATE	LOCATION	TIME OF DAY

WEATHER		

DURATION		
Start Time:	End Time:	Steps:

DISTANCE		

WATER		
Before Walk:	During Walk:	After Walk:

MOOD	
Before Walk:	After Walk:

ENERGY	
Before Walk:	After Walk:

NOTES

Walking Wellness Tracker

DATE	LOCATION	TIME OF DAY

WEATHER

DURATION		
Start Time:	End Time:	Steps:

DISTANCE

WATER		
Before Walk:	During Walk:	After Walk:

MOOD	
Before Walk:	After Walk:

ENERGY	
Before Walk:	After Walk:

NOTES

Walking Wellness Tracker

DATE	LOCATION	TIME OF DAY

WEATHER

DURATION

Start Time:	End Time:	Steps:

DISTANCE

WATER

Before Walk:	During Walk:	After Walk:

MOOD

Before Walk:	After Walk:

ENERGY

Before Walk:	After Walk:

NOTES

Walking Wellness Tracker

DATE	LOCATION	TIME OF DAY

WEATHER

DURATION

Start Time:	End Time:	Steps:

DISTANCE

WATER

Before Walk:	During Walk:	After Walk:

MOOD

Before Walk:	After Walk:

ENERGY

Before Walk:	After Walk:

NOTES

Thank you for purchasing Walk Your Way Calm

Visit our online store to find more great products
from Prevention and save 20% off your next purchase.

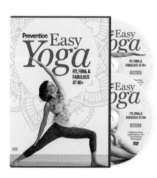  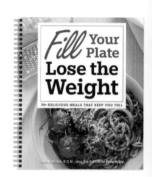

HEARST